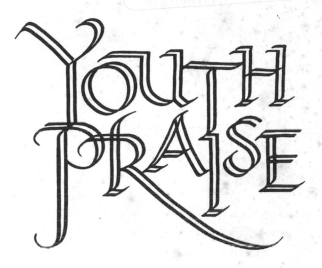

A new collection of Christian hymns, songs, choruses and spirituals, compiled by the Reverend Michael A. Baughen. Assisted by the Reverend Richard Bewes

FALCON BOOKS * LONDON

FIRST PUBLISHED MARCH 1966

REPRINTED JUNE 1966, NOVEMBER 1966, DECEMBER 1966,
MARCH 1967, OCTOBER 1967, JANUARY 1968, JULY 1968,
NOVEMBER 1968, MARCH 1969

Standard Book Numbers: 85491 800 0 (Fabric)
85491 801 9 (Boards)

Overseas Agents

EMU Book Agency Ltd, 511 Kent Street, Sydney NSW,
Australia

CSSM and Crusader Bookroom Society Ltd, 177 Manchester Street, Christchurch,
New Zealand

Sunday School Centre Wholesale, Box 3020, Cape Town,
South Africa

Published as a Falcon Book for the Church Pastoral-Aid Society, 32 Fleet Street, London, EC4.
Printed and Bound in Great Britain by
Bookprint Limited, Crawley, Sussex

COLOPHON: HUGH SPENDLOVE

CONTENTS

MY LIPS SHALL GREATLY REJOICE
WHEN I SING UNTO THEE;
AND MY SOUL,
WHICH THOU HAST REDEEMED

Psalm 71.23

INTRODUCTION

THIS BOOK has been compiled to try to meet the evident need for a composite youth music book in Christian youth groups of many kinds. Its purpose is not to provide 'musical entertainment with a religious flavour', but the provision of words and tunes, in adequate number and variety, to allow contemporary expression of youth praise and prayer and worship.

No one is expected to find every item in the book to his particular taste. The compiler and his helpers have drawn together choruses and songs already in use in widely different situations, and from different parts of this country. They have also added a considerable quantity of new material, and a number of translations. Tastes vary widely in the matter of Christian youth music, and the aim has been to provide a book in which all tastes will find a good selection which they can sing.

The quality of music as well as of words shows considerable variation from page to page, and this again is to serve the differing needs of those who will use the book. Some groups have pianists (and guitarists) who 'do their best' and who need simple music; others have accomplished musicians who can manage something more difficult. On the whole, it has been thought best to offer music suitable for the less able musician, in the belief that others will be able to develop their own harmonies and arrangements.

The book is a mixture of old and new, and is classified into sections so that it can be used purposefully rather than 'just for the sake of singing'. Experiments for two years before publication have shown the value of this arrangement, although any classification of chorus music must be somewhat arbitrary.

A list of acknowledgements follows, which must be read in conjunction with the acknowledgement of sources that will be found against words and music at the foot of each page. Most items in the book are copyright, and the compiler and publishers gratefully acknowledge many kindnesses in permitting the inclusion of copyright material. Every effort has been made to trace copyright-holders, but any errors or omissions will gladly be put right at the first opportunity.

ACKNOWLEDGEMENTS

THE EARLIER STAGES of the work were in the hands of a committee which included the Revs. R. T. Bewes, M. H. Botting, M. D. Drury, J. M. Filby, C. P. Gane, K. W. Habershon, J. F. Perry, G. H. Reid, T. O. Walker, and D. C. K. Watson. We benefited greatly from the interest and encouragement of the Revs. J. R. W. Stott and T. Dudley-Smith.

The main task of the compiler since then has been greatly eased by the assiduous work of the Rev. R. T. Bewes, who has been responsible for the inclusion of most of the gospel songs and spirituals to be found in the book.

Musical arrangements have been undertaken by a number of helpers, including notably the Rev. N. L. Warren, Messrs M. C. T. Strover, G. R. Timms, D. G. Wilson, Mrs J. B. Wooldridge, and Miss P. C. Butler. Several people, including J. Roberts, have helped with the guitar chords, but the great majority of these are the work of S. G. Kitchen and A. Betts-Brown.

We are grateful to those who have given unstinted clerical help at different stages, including Mrs H. P. Brooks, Mrs R. E. Dyton, Miss E. M. Hopper, Miss P. Monk, and Miss M. A. Ogden; and we thankfully acknowledge the continual help and guidance of our printers, Mr F. W. Birkenshaw and Mr S. G. Kitchen.

My thanks go to all who have helped in so many ways, and my final, special thanks are for my wife, who has patiently borne with me, and with much hospitality for others, during the whole time of the preparation of this book.

M.A.B.

Praise and Thanks

1. We will sing

Music: G. Brattle
Words: L.C. Barnes

We will sing of our Re-deem-er, He's our King:___

All His glo-ry, all His praise to you___ we bring;

With our hearts and with our voi-ces Him we sing,___

We love the Lord, we love His Word, He's our King.___

2. Come and Praise

Words: Anon.
Music: Traditional
arr. P.C. Butler and D.G. Wilson

Start with Chorus

Chorus   Come and praise the Lord our King, Hallelujah,
Come and praise the Lord our King, Hallelujah.

1. Christ was born in Bethlehem, Hallelujah,
Son of God and Son of Man, Hallelujah:
Chorus

2. He grew up an earthly child, Hallelujah,
Of the world, but undefiled, Hallelujah:
Chorus

3. Jesus died at Calvary, Hallelujah,
Rose again triumphantly, Hallelujah:
Chorus

4. He will cleanse us from our sin, Hallelujah,
If we live by faith in Him, Hallelujah:
Chorus

5. We will live with Him one day, Hallelujah,
And for ever with Him stay, Hallelujah:
Chorus

3. Tell out, my soul!

Words: T. Dudley-Smith
Music: M.A. Baughen

With a swing

1. Tell out, my soul, the greatness of the Lord; Un - numbered

F   Dm7   C   F

bless - ings give my spir- it voice; Ten - der to me the promise

Dm   Bb   G9 G7   C   F   Bb F C   F7

of His Word; In God my Saviour shall my heart re - joice.

Bb Bb6 Bb Bbm F Bb F6 C C6 C7 F

2. Tell out, my soul, the greatness of His Name!
Make known His might, the deeds His arm has done;
His mercy sure, from age to age the same;
His Holy Name — the Lord, the Mighty One.

3. Tell out, my soul, the greatness of His might!
Powers and dominions lay their glory by.
Proud hearts and stubborn wills are put to flight,
The hungry fed, the humble lifted high.

4. Tell out, my soul, the glories of His Word!
Firm is His promise, and His mercy sure.
Tell out, my soul, the greatness of the Lord
To children's children and for evermore!

4. There's no greater name

Words and Music: M.A. Baughen

With a good swing – fairly fast

There's no great - er Name than Je - sus, Name of Him who came to save us, In that sav - ing Name of Je - sus Ev - 'ry knee should bow. Let ev - 'ry - thing that is 'neath the ground, Let ev - 'ry - thing in the world a - round,

5. When morning gilds the skies

Words: Anon. 19th Century German
tr. E. Caslon
Music: D.G. Wilson

2. Be this, when day is past,
   Of all my thoughts the last,
   'May Jesus Christ be praised!'
   The night becomes as day,
   When from the heart we say:
   'May Jesus Christ be praised!'

3. Does sadness fill my mind,
   A solace here I find,
   'May Jesus Christ be praised!'
   When evil thoughts molest,
   With this I shield my breast:
   'May Jesus Christ be praised!'

4. To God, the Word on high,
   The hosts of angels cry,
   'May Jesus Christ be praised!'
   Let mortals, too, upraise
   Their voice in hymns of praise:
   'May Jesus Christ be praised!'

5. Let earth's wide circle round
   In joyful notes resound,
   'May Jesus Christ be praised!'
   Let earth and sea and sky,
   From depth to height, reply:
   'May Jesus Christ be praised!'

6. Be this while life is mine
   My canticle divine,
   'May Jesus Christ be praised!'
   Be this the eternal song,
   Through all the ages long:
   'May Jesus Christ be praised!'

6. There is joy in the presence

Words and Music: G.R. Timms

one sin-ner that re - pen - teth,___ Praise the Lord for His love and for His

Am7   D   D7   G   Gb+   F6   E7   Am   E7   Am   A7

heav- en a - bove, where His saints shall re - joice for   ev - er.___

D   D7   G   C   Am7   D   G

© G.R. Timms 1964 By kind permission

7. I'm singing for my Lord

Words: J. Smith
Music: R. Harper

I'm sing-ing for my   Lord_____   ev-'ry-where I   go,

C7   F   F7   Bb   F

Sing - ing of His wondrous love   that the world may know

Bb   F   G7   C

How He saved a | wretch like me | by His death on | Cal - var - y: I'm

F   F7   B♭

singing for my | Lord___ | ev - 'ry - where I | go. | go.

F   A7   Dm   G7   C7   F   F

2.   I'm singing, but sometimes heavy is the rod,
For this world is not a friend to the grace of God;
Yet I sing the whole day long, for He fills my heart with song,
I'm singing for my Lord everywhere I go.

3.   I'm singing for the lost just because I know
Jesus Christ, whose precious blood washes white as snow;
If my songs to Him can bring some lost soul I'll gladly sing:
I'm singing for my Lord everywhere I go.

4.   I'm singing, for the saints as they journey home;
Soon they'll reach that happy land where they'll never roam,
And with me they'll join and sing praises to our Lord and King:
I'm singing for my Lord everywhere I go.

8. Sweet is the work

Words: I. Watts
Music: H. Parker

Sweet is the work, my God, my King, To praise Thy
Name, give thanks and sing, To show Thy love by
morn - ing light, And talk of all Thy truth at night.

© Joshua Duckworth Ltd, Colne, Lancs   By kind permission

9. We sing a loving Jesus

Words: S. Doodney
Music: N.L. Warren

1. We sing a lov - ing Jesus

Who left His throne a - bove And came to earth to ransom The
chil - dren of His love;___ It is an oft - told story,
And yet we love to_ tell How Christ, the King of glo-ry
Once deigned with man to dwell, face

2. We sing a lowly Jesus
No kingly crown He had
His heart was bowed with anguish
His face was marred and sad;
In deep humiliation
He came, His work to do
O Lord of our salvation
Let us be humble too.

3. We sing a mighty Jesus
Whose voice could raise the dead
The sightless eyes He opened
The famished souls He fed.
Thou camest to deliver
Mankind from sin and shame;
Redeemer and life-giver,
We praise Thy Holy Name!

4. We sing a coming Jesus
The time is drawing near
When Christ with all His angels
In glory shall appear.
Lord, save us, we entreat Thee,
In this Thy day of grace,
That we may gladly meet Thee,
And see Thee face to face.

B

10. Christ triumphant

Words: M. Saward
Music: M.A. Baughen

With triumphant vigour

Christ tri-um-phant ev-er reign-ing, Sav-iour, Master, King,___ Lord of heav'n, our lives sus-tain-ing, Hear us as we sing.___ Yours the glo-ry and the crown___ The high re-nown___ The e-ter-nal name.___

2. Word incarnate, truth revealing,
Son of Man on earth,
Power and majesty concealing
By Your humble birth.
Yours the glory and the crown–
The high renown–
The eternal name.

3. Suffering servant, scorned, ill-treated,
Victim crucified,
Death is through the cross defeated
Sinners justified.
Yours the glory and the crown–
The high renown–
The eternal name.

4. Priestly King, enthroned for ever
High in heaven above,
Sin and death and hell shall never
Stifle hymns of love.
Yours the glory and the crown–
The high renown–
The eternal name.

5. So, our hearts and voices raising
Through the ages long,
Ceaselessly upon you gazing
This shall be our song.
Yours the glory and the crown–
The high renown–
The eternal name.

CHRIST TRIUMPHANT Suggested accompaniment for verses 2 & 4 arranged by D. G. Wilson.

© M. Saward and M.A. Baughen 1964 By kind permission

CHRIST TRIUMPHANT Suggested arrangement for verse 3 by H. Clifton.

With a 2 bar swing

© M. Saward and M.A. Baughen 1964 By kind permission

11. Lord of the cross

Words: **M. Saward**
Music: **M.A. Baughen**

1. Lord of the cross of shame,
Set my cold heart a-flame
With love for you, my Saviour and my Master;
Who on that lonely day
Bore all my sins away,
And saved me from the judgement and disaster.

2. Lord of the empty tomb,
Born of a virgin's womb,
Triumphant over death, its power defeated;
How gladly now I sing
Your praise, my risen King,
And worship you, in heaven's splendour seated.

3. Lord of my life today,
Teach me to live and pray
As one who knows the joy of sins forgiven;
So may I ever be,
Now and eternally,
United with the citizens of heaven.

12. Jesus Christ is my Lord and King

Words and Music: M.A. Baughen
arr. P.C. Butler

Start with chorus

Chorus   Jesus Christ is my Lord and King,
To Him honour and glory bring,
Join the mighty host in heav'n above
and praise His gracious Name.

1.   He who now is reigning in majesty
Stooped to bear our sin in humility
There on Calvary - Jesus died for me -
Died to set me free - eternally!
Chorus

2.   Justified by faith we have peace with God
Fellowship with Him through our Saviour's blood,
Wonder though it be - sons of God are we -
In His family - eternally!
Chorus

13. Thank you

Words: M.G. Schneider
tr. and adapted S. Lonsdale and M.A. Baughen
Music: M.G. Schneider
set out in key changes by D.G Wilson

Thank You_ for ev-'ry new good morn-ing, Thank You_ for ev-'ry fresh new day,

Thank You_ that I may cast my burdens Wholly on to You.

Thank You_ for ev-'ry friend I have, Lord, Thank You_ for ev-'ry-one I know,

Thank You when I can | feel forgiveness To my greatest | foe.   (Piano)

F   F7   Cm7 F7   Bb   Bbm   F   C7   F   C#7

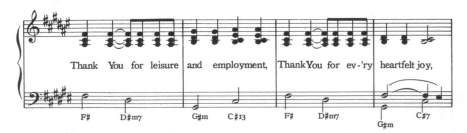

Thank You for leisure | and employment, Thank You for ev-'ry | heartfelt joy,

F#   D#m7   G#m   C#13   F#   D#m7   G#m   C#7

Thank You for all that | makes me happy And for mel - o - | dy.   (Piano)

F#   F#7 C#m7 F#7   B   Bm   F#   C#7

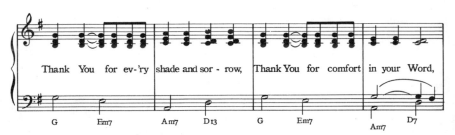

Thank You for ev-'ry | shade and sor - row, Thank You for comfort | in your Word,

G   Em7   Am7   D13   G   Em7   Am7   D7

Thank You that I am | guided by You Ev-'ry-where I | go.   (Piano)

G   G7   Dm7 G7   C   Cm   G   D11   G   Eb7

Thank You_ for grace to know Your gos - pel, Thank You_ for all Your

Ab   Fm7   Bb m7   Eb13   Ab   Fm7

Spir - it's power, Thank You_ for Your un-fail - ing love Which reaches far and

Bbm7   Eb7   Ab   Ab7   Ebm7   Ab7   Db   Dbm   Ab   Eb7

near.   (Piano)   Thank You_ for free and full sal - va - tion,

Ab   E7   A   F#m7   Bm   E13

Thank You_ for grace to hold it fast, Thank You,_ O Lord, I

A   F#m7   Bm   E7   A   A7   Em7   A7

want to thank You, That I'm free to | **1** thank!_ | **2** thank!

D   Dm   A   E7   A   E7   A

14. Oh, thank the Lord

Words: Anon
Music: Traditional German air

Oh, thank the Lord, oh thank the Lord, Give Him the praise for He is good; Be-cause His mer-cy does en-dure, His faith-ful-ness is ev-er sure; Oh thank the Lord, oh thank the Lord, Give Him the praise for He is good.

15. How great Thou art

Music: Old Melody
Words: N. J. Clayton

Majestically

O Lord most high, Thou ho - ly God and Sav - iour, Thy pow'r and might are more than tongue can tell, But great-er far the love that planned sal-va - tion And saved the lost from sin and death and hell.

CHORUS

O God of Love, O God of Cal - va - ry, How great Thou art! How great Thou art! In all the world there is no one like Thee, How great Thou art, How great Thou art!

2. Once far from God, an alien and a stranger,
   Of hope bereft, a sinner lost and lone,
   But Jesus came to rescue from the danger,
   To give us life He sacrificed His own.
   Chorus:

3. In mercy rich, in love and grace abounding,
   When we were dead in trespasses and sins,
   Thine only Son for us was freely given,
   How great Thou art! in Thee our life begins.
   Chorus:

At the Beginning of a Meeting

16. Open Thou my eyes

Words and Music: G.R. Timms

17. Lord, you look

Words and Music: H. Banter
tr. S. Lonsdale and M.A. Baughen

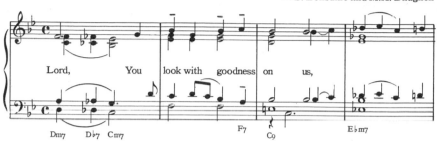

Lord, You look with goodness on us,

Lord, You pour Your love up - on us,

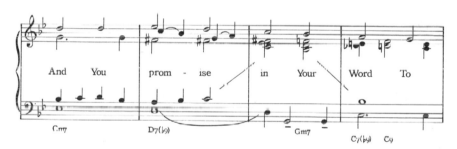

And You prom - ise in Your Word To

hear us when we pray.

18. Come among us, Lord

Words and Music: **G. Brattle**

© G. Brattle By kind permission

19. By blue Galilee

Words and Music: E.H. Swinstead

By blue Ga - li - lee Je - sus walked of old,

By blue Ga li lee wondrous things He told.

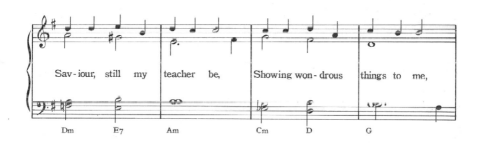

Sav-iour, still my teacher be, Showing won-drous things to me,

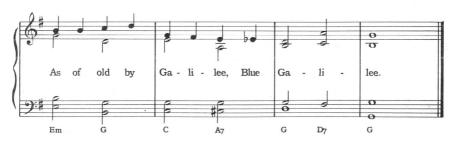

As of old by Ga - li - lee, Blue Ga - li - lee.

20. Turn your eyes

Words and Music: H.H. Lemmel

Turn your eyes up-on Je - sus, Look full in His won-der-ful face;___ And the things of earth will grow

strange-ly dim In the light of His glo-ry and grace.___

© 1922 Renewal 1950 by H.H. Lemmel
Assigned to Singspiration Inc.   All rights reserved   By kind permission

21. Break Thou the bread of Life

Words: M.A. Lathbury
Music: W.F. Sherwin

Break Thou the Bread of Life, dear Lord, to me, As Thou didst

break the loaves be-side the sea; Be-yond the sa-cred page

I seek Thee, Lord; My spirit longs for Thee, O liv-ing Word!

22. Speak to us, Lord

Words and Music: G. Brattle

Speak to us, Lord, in this brief hour to-day;

Give light up-on the written word we pray; Stir heart and

mind to heed and to__ o-bey, For this we plead.

C

23. Triumphant victor

Words and Music: G. Brattle

Tri - um - phant vic - tor, life giv - ing Sav - iour,

Ris'n from the dead on that first Eas - ter day.

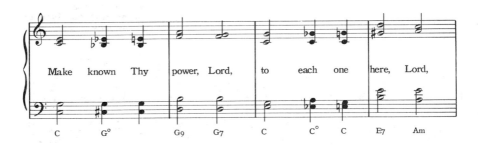

Make known Thy power, Lord, to each one here, Lord,

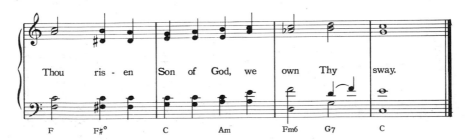

Thou ris - en Son of God, we own Thy sway.

God's Love and Grace
24. God's love is wonderful

Words and Music: S.E. Cox

God's love is wonder-ful, God's love is wonder-ful,— Wonderful that

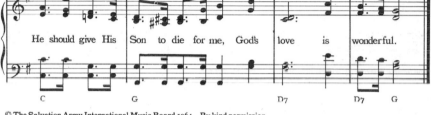

He should give His Son to die for me, God's love is wonderful.

© The Salvation Army International Music Board 1964 By kind permission

25. On Calvary's tree

Words: A.W. Edsor
Music (melody): A.E. Walton
arr. A.W. Edsor

On Calv'ry's tree He died for me, That I His love might know

To set me free He died for me, That's why I love Him so.

© Melody only copyright J.R. Lafleur & Son Ltd: this arrangement and words copyright The Victory Press Ltd. By kind permission

26. Wonderful grace of Jesus

Words and Music: H. Lillenas

1. Won-der-ful grace of Je - sus, great-er than all my sin;
2. Won-der-ful grace of Je - sus, reach-ing to all the lost;
3. Won-der-ful grace of Je - sus, reach-ing the most de - filed,

How shall my tongue de - scribe it, where shall its praise be - gin?
By it I have been par - doned, saved to the ut - ter - most,
By its transforming pow - er, making him God's own child,

Tak - ing a - way my bur - den, set - ting my spir - it free,
Chains have been torn a - sun - der, giv - ing me lib - er - ty,
Pur - chas - ing peace and hea - ven, for all e - ter - ni - ty,

For the won-der-ful grace of Je - sus reach - es me.
For the won-der-ful grace of Je - sus reach - es me:
And the won-der-ful grace of Je - sus reach - es me:

CHORUS

Won-der-ful the matchless grace of Je - sus, Deep - er
the grace of Je - sus, Deeper than the

*Guitar players accompanying this hymn may prefer key D as indicated by chord symbols in brackets.

27. Higher than the hills

Words and Music: N. J. Clayton

High - er than the hills, Deep - er than the sea,
Broad - er than the skies a-bove is my Re - deem - er's love for me;
To His cross of shame, Je - sus free - ly came,
Bear - ing all my sin and sor - row Won - drous love!

28. In the garden Gethsemane

Words and Music: J. Jurgens
tr. and adapted S. Lonsdale and M.A. Baughen

Moderato

1. In the garden Gethsemane Christ Jesus knelt alone, With burdened heart and pain ahead He faced the cross alone; Never was a man forsaken In such a way as this In the garden Gethsemane Christ Jesus knelt alone.

2. In the garden Gethsemane
Christ Jesus knelt alone,
Yet where were His disciples when
He faced the cross alone?
Eyes were heavy, sleep was easy,
They let Him watch alone
In the garden Gethsemane:
Christ Jesus knelt alone.

3. In the garden Gethsemane
Christ Jesus knelt alone,
"Father" He said, "Thy will be done"
Christ Jesus knelt alone;
Then the cross for our salvation
For us then to atone:
In the garden Gethsemane
Christ Jesus knelt alone.

4. In the garden Gethsemane
Christ Jesus knelt alone,
And now today He looks to us
To those He calls His own;
Are we watching? Are we praying?
Or are we failing Him?
In the garden Gethsemane
Christ Jesus knelt alone.

29. The grace of the Lord

Words: J.S. Holden
Music: C.H.M. Foster

The grace of the Lord, like a fath - om - less sea Suf - fi -cient for you, suf - fi - cient for me, Is ten - der and patient and bound - less and free Suf - fi - cient for ev - 'ry need.

30. Living, He loved me

Words: J.W. Chapman
Music: C.H. Marsh

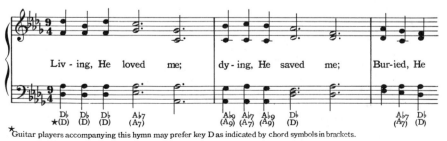

Liv - ing, He loved me; dy - ing, He saved me; Bur - ied, He

★Guitar players accompanying this hymn may prefer key D as indicated by chord symbols in brackets.

car - ried my sins far a - way;___ Ris- ing, He jus - ti - fied

G♭
(G)
E♭7
(B7)
E♭7
(E7)
A♭
(A)
A♭7
(A7)
D♭
(D)
A♭7
(A7)

cresc.

free - ly for ev - er; One day He's com - ing — O glo - ri - ous day!___

rit.

D♭
(D)
G♭
(G)
B♭7
(B7)
E♭
(E)
E♭7
(E7)
A♭7
(A7)
D♭
(D)

31. For God so loved the world

Words: F. Townsend
Music: A.B. Smith

For God so lov'd the world, He gave His on - ly Son, To

G
E
E7
A
A7

die on Calvary's tree, From sin to set me free; Some day He's coming

D
D7
G

back, What glo - ry that will be, Won - der-ful His love to me.

E7
A
A 7
D7
G

32. Two thousand years

Words: A. Boddington and R.T. Bewes
Music: R.T. Bewes
arr. M.C.T. Strover

1. It was just two thousand years a-go He walked thro' Ga-li-

-lee, The e-ter-nal God had stepped be-low In human form to

be; Born of a low-ly He-brew maid, A car-pen-ter He
gives me peace and pur-pose true, A power that's old but

was by trade; He came down, Two thou-sand years a - go:_____
ev - er new; God came down, Two thou-sand years a - go._____

They tell of Je-sus' glo-ry, Who met Him in the way; And it

is no id-le sto-ry, for He lives in__ me to - day: He__

2. It was just two thousand years ago
He died on Calvary;
It was for sin He suffered so,
Though innocent was He.
My sin and guilt lay on His head;
My penalty He bore instead;
He suffered,
Two thousand years ago.

Chorus

3. It was just two thousand years ago
An empty tomb was found;
The stone was rolled away we know,
The powers of hell are bound;
My risen Lord is now on high,
He lives that we may never die,
He triumphed!
Two thousand years ago:

Chorus

33. Oh, the love that drew

Words: W.R. Newell
Music: D.B. Turner

Oh, the love that drew sal-va-tion's plan! Oh, the grace that brought it down to man! Oh, the might-y gulf that God did span at Cal-va-ry! Mer-cy there was great, and grace was free; Par-don there was mul-ti-plied to me; There my burdened soul found li-ber-ty, at Cal-va-ry.

34. Just because

Words and Music: A.E. Kelly

1. Just be-cause He set His heart on me, Just be-cause His pow'r could

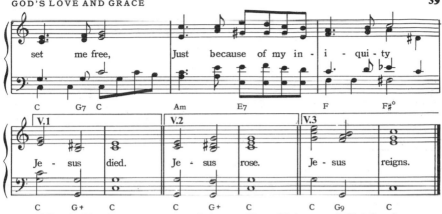

set me free, Just because of my in - i - qui - ty

C G7 C Am E7 F F#°

V.1 Je - sus died. V.2 Je - sus rose. V.3 Je - sus reigns.

C G+ C C G+ C C G9 C

2. When by Him the ransom was supplied,
When by Him the debt was satisfied,
When by Him we could be justified
Jesus rose.

3. Now of Calvary each Christian sings,
Now with praise to Christ all heaven rings,
Now He's Lord of Lords and King of Kings
Jesus reigns.

35. His compassions fail not

Words and Music: G.R. Timms

His com - pas - sions fail___ not,___ fail___ not, ___

C Em7 F G C G7 C Dm7 G7

His com - pas-sions fail___ not,___ They are new ev - 'ry morning.

C Em7 D9 Em Am E+ C6 C° Dm7 Am6 Dm G7 C

Great is Thy faithfulness, Great is Thy faithfulness;

Am G7 C Am E7 Am D7 G7

Dm7

His com-pas-sions fail___ not, They are new ev - 'ry day.

F Em Fmaj7 G7 Am C7 F C C° G7 C

36. Can it be true?

Words and Music: Brother William
arr. The Venturers

2. And day by day You still return this way;
   But we recall there was a debt to pay:
   Out of Your love for Your own world above,
   You left that holy thing, Your endless love to prove.

3. Can it be true, the things they did to You-
   The death, the shame, and were Your friends so few?
   Yet You returned again alive and free-
   Can it be true, my Lord, it had to be.

37. I know a fount

Words and Music: O. Cooke

I know a fount where sins are wash'd a - way, (a - way); I know a place where night is turned to day (to day); Bur - dens are lift - ed, blind eyes made to see:— There's a won - der work - ing pow'r in the blood of Cal - va - ry.

38. Tell me, Lord Jesus

Words and Music: M. Snowdon

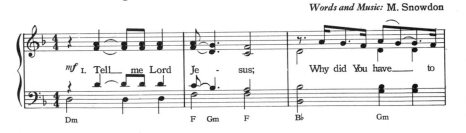

1. Tell me Lord Je - sus; Why did You have to

die,__ Mas-ter? Tell me Lord Je - sus:__ Why did You have to

Am F Dm Gm Bb F Gm C13

1 & 2 *(Continuation)* **Slower** 3 *(Fine)*

die? And You die? came down to earth from

F Am E7 F Am Em7 Am

heaven will-ing-ly, There at Cal-var-y, On the curs-ed tree,

G Dm E Am Em

There You died for me. There You died for me. *D.C.*

Dm6 Dm E D E Am C7 F A7

2. Pride, sin and wrong in us,
   That cut us off from God, our Father,
   When we were bound in sin,
   That's when You came to die.

   And You came down to earth,
   From heaven willingly,
   There at Calvary,
   On the cursed tree,
   There You died for me,
   There You died for me.

3. You came to set us free,
   That's why You had to die, Master,
   To give us liberty,
   That's why You had to die.

D

39. New every morning

Words and Music: **M.A. Baughen**
arr. **W. Wooldridge**

1. New!_____ ev - 'ry morning it's new!_____ The love of
2. New!_____ ev - 'ry morning it's new!_____ The love of
3. New!_____ ev - 'ry morning it's new!_____ The love of

G   Em7   C   D7

To Coda
(3rd time)

God   to me is   won-der-ful - ly   new!_____
Cal - va - ry is   won-der-ful - ly   new!_____
God   to me is   won-der-ful - ly   new!_____

G   D7   G   D7

New!_____ ev - 'ry morning it's new!_____ The mer - cy
New!_____ ev - 'ry morning it's new!_____ The mer - cy

G   Em7   C   D7

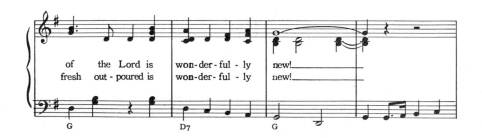

of   the Lord is   won-der-ful - ly   new!_____
fresh out - poured is   won-der- ful - ly   new!_____

G   D7   G

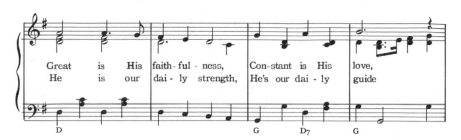

Great is His faith-ful - ness, Con-stant is His love,
He is our dai - ly strength, He's our dai - ly guide

D   G   D7   G

Great is His sav- ing pow'r Coming from a - bove!
If we will wait on Him And in Him a - bide!

D   A7   D   G   A7   D7

D.C.

 CODA

New!_____ ev - 'ry morning it's new!_____ The mer - cy

G6   G7   C6   Cm

of the Lord is won-der - ful - ly new!

G   D7   G

40. Jesu, lover of my soul

Words C. Wesley
Music: D.G. Wilson

1. Je - su, lov - er of my soul, Let me to Thy bo - som fly, While the near- er wat - ers roll, While the tempest still is high, Hide me, O my Sav - iour, hide, Till the storm of life is past; Safe in - to the haven guide; O re - ceive my soul at last!

2. Other refuge have I none;
   Hangs my helpless soul on Thee;
   Leave,ah, leave me not alone;
   Still support and comfort me.
   All my trust on Thee is stayed;
   All my help from Thee I bring;
   Cover my defenceless head
   With the shadow of Thy wing.

3. Thou, O Christ, art all I want;
   More than all in Thee I find;
   Raise the fallen, cheer the faint,
   Heal the sick and lead the blind.
   Just and holy is Thy Name,
   I am all unrighteousness;
   False and full of sin I am,
   Thou art full of truth and grace.

4. Plenteous grace with Thee is found,
   Grace to cover all my sin;
   Let the healing streams abound;
   Make and keep me pure within.
   Thou of life the fountain art,
   Freely let me take of Thee;
   Spring Thou up within my heart,
   Rise to all eternity.

41. Ride on, ride on in majesty!

Words: H.H. Milman
Music: D.G. Wilson

1. Ride on, ride on in ma - jes - ty!___
Hark, all the tribes Ho - san - na cry;___
O Sav - iour meek, pur - sue Thy road___
With palms and scat - tered garments strowed.

2. Ride on, ride on in majesty!
In lowly pomp ride on to die;
O Christ, Thy triumphs now begin
O'er captive death and conquered sin.

3. Ride on, ride on in majesty!
The angel armies of the sky
Look down with sad and wondering eyes
To see the approaching sacrifice.

4. Ride on, ride on in majesty!
Thy last, Thy fiercest strife is nigh;
The Father on His sapphire throne
Awaits His own anointed Son.

5. Ride on, ride on in majesty!
In lowly pomp ride on to die;
Bow Thy meek head to mortal pain,
Then take, O God, Thy power, and reign.

Testimony

42. Jesus died for me

Words and Music: G.R. Timms

43. There is a Name

Words: F. Whitfield
Music: W.H. Rudd

1. There is a Name I love to hear, I love to speak its worth; It sounds like music in my ear, The sweet-est Name on earth:

CHORUS
Oh, how I love the Saviour's Name, Oh, how I love the Saviour's Name, How I
(Altos) How I love the Saviour's Name, How love the Saviour's Name, How I
Oh how I love the Saviour's Name, The sweet-est Name on earth (on earth):
love I love the Saviour's Name,

2. It tells me of a Saviour's love,
    Who died to set me free;
    It tells me of His precious blood,
    The sinner's perfect plea:
    Chorus

3. It tells of one whose loving heart
    Can feel my deepest woe,
    Who in my sorrow bears a part
    That none can bear below:
    Chorus

4. It bids my trembling heart rejoice,
    It dries each rising tear;
    It tells me in a 'still, small voice'
    To trust and never fear.
    Chorus

5. Jesus, the Name I love so well,
    The Name I love to hear!
    No saint on earth its worth can tell,
    No heart conceive how dear!
    Chorus

44. Christt for me

Words and Music: A. Burns

Christ for me,——yes,it's Christ for me,——

He's my Saviour,my Lord and King; I'm so hap-py I shout and sing;

Ev-'ry day as I go my way it is Christ for me.——

45. 'Tis marvellous and wonderful

Words and Music: C.H. Morris

1. The Saviour has come in His might - y pow'r, And spo - ken

peace to my soul,—— And all of my life from that ve - ry hour I've

2. From glory to glory He leads me on,
From grace to grace ev'ry day,
And brighter and brighter the glory dawns
While pressing my homeward way,
While pressing my homeward way.

Chorus

3. If fellowship here with my Lord can be
So inexpressibly sweet,
O what will it be when His face we see,
When round the white throne we meet,
When round the white throne we meet?

Chorus

46. Life is wonderful now

Words and Music: I. Sutherland

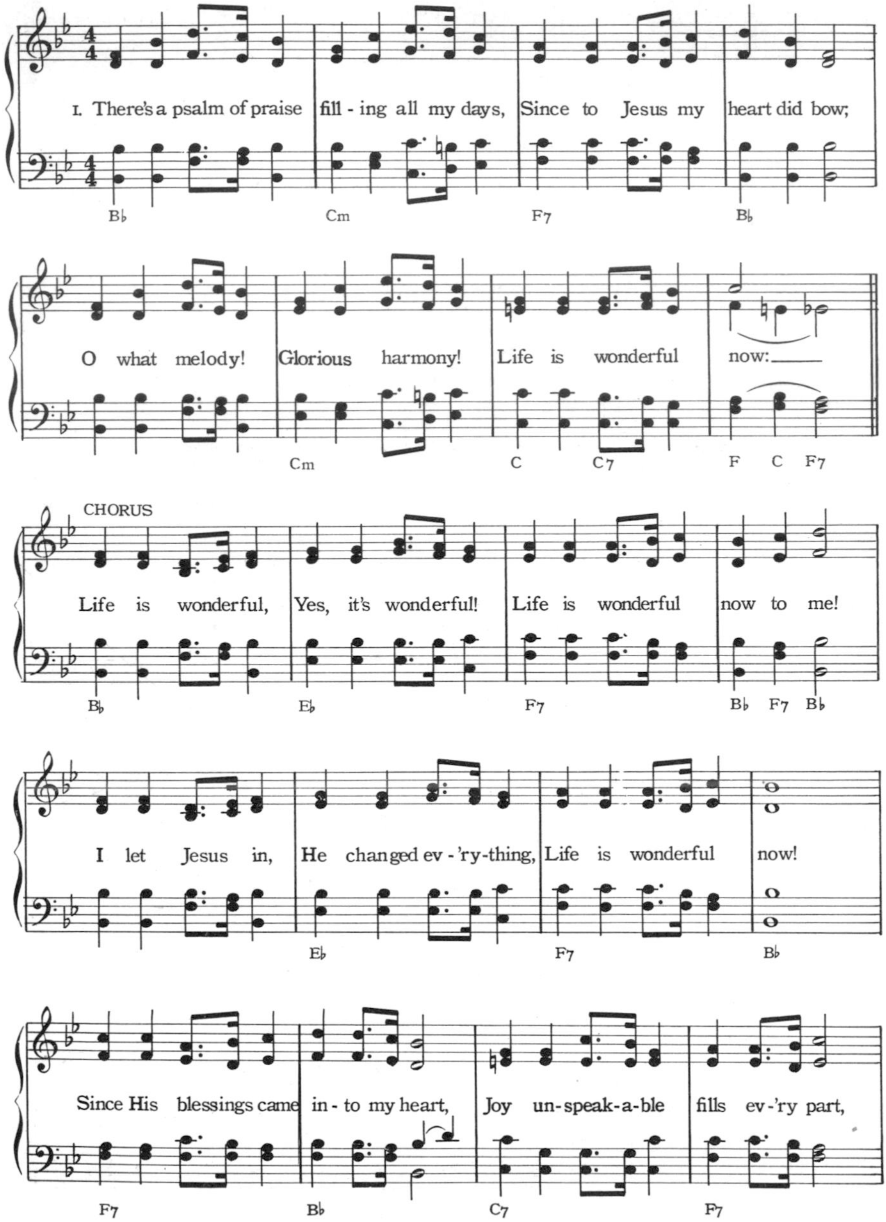

1. There's a psalm of praise fill - ing all my days, Since to Jesus my heart did bow;
B♭ Cm F7 B♭
O what melody! Glorious harmony! Life is wonderful now:
Cm C C7 F C F7
CHORUS
Life is wonderful, Yes, it's wonderful! Life is wonderful now to me!
B♭ E♭ F7 B♭ F7 B♭
I let Jesus in, He changed ev - 'ry-thing, Life is wonderful now!
E♭ F7 B♭
Since His blessings came in - to my heart, Joy un-speak-a-ble fills ev-'ry part,
F7 B♭ C7 F7

And I want to live | for my Lord;___ | Life is won-der-ful | now!

Bb | F7 Bb | Cm | F7 | Bb F7 | Bb

2. All is happiness, gone is my distress,
   Peace and vict'ry He does endow;
   Since my Saviour came, I can't be the same;
   Life is wonderful now:
   Chorus

3. All my life is praise for His wondrous grace,
   I will serve the Lord, this my vow;
   Jesus came to me, and He set me free;
   Life is wonderful now:
   Chorus

47. Jesus came from Heaven

Words and Music: G.R. Timms

Je - sus came from | hea - ven | With a humble | birth,

Db | Db° | Gb6 | Bb7

Took man's form up - | on Him To | live with us on | earth.

Gb | Fm Ab7(add6) | Bbm Eb7 | Ab

Je - sus grew to | man - hood | In God's per-fect | plan,

Db | Db° | Gb6 | Bb

48. In my need Jesus found me

Words and Music: G. Brattle

In my need Je-sus found me, Put His strong arm a-round me, Brought me safe home, In-to the shel-ter of the fold. Grac-ious shep-herd that sought me, Pre-cious life-blood that brought me Out of the night, In-to the light, and nigh to God.

49. Gone! Gone!

Words and Music: H. Griggs

Gone! Gone! Gone! Gone! Yes, my sins are gone. Now my soul is free and in my heart's a song. Bur-ied in the deepest sea. Yes, that's good enough for me. I shall live e-ter-nal-ly. Praise God! my sins are gone.

50. I'm not ashamed

Words and Music: G.R. Timms

I'm not a-shamed not a-shamed of the gos-pel of

Christ For it is the pow'r of God un-to— sal-
-va-tion To— ev-'ry-one to— ev-'ry-one that be-liev-eth

51. Joined to the vine

Words and Music: R. McCurdy Jones

Joined to the vine as a branch of the tree,
Cleansed by His word that He's spoken to me, Stemmed in His love as He
wants me to be: Bear-ing the fruit of the Lord.—

52. He lives!

Words and Music: A.H. Ackley

He lives!___ He lives!___ Christ Je - sus lives to - day!___ He
walks with me and talks with me A - long life's nar - row way.___ He
lives!___ He lives,___ Sal - va - tion to im - part!___ You
ask me how I know He lives— He lives with - in my heart.___

53. Thou shalt guide me with Thy counsel

Words and Music: G.R. Timms

Thou shalt guide me with Thy coun - sel___ And af - ter

E

54. Now I belong to Jesus

Words and Music: N. J. Clayton

1. Je-sus my Lord will love me for ev-er, From Him no pow'r of e-vil can se-ver He gave His life to ran-som my soul, Now I be-long to Him:

CHORUS

Now I be-long to Je-sus, Je-sus be-longs to me,

Not for the years of time a-lone, But for e-ter-ni-ty.

2. Once I was lost in sin's degradation,
   Jesus came down to bring me salvation;
   Lifted me up from sorrow and shame,
   Now I belong to Him:
   Chorus

3. Joy floods my soul for Jesus has saved me,
   Freed me from sin that long had enslaved me,
   His precious blood He gave to redeem,
   Now I belong to Him:
   Chorus

© N. J. Clayton 1943 By kind permission

55. All that thrills

Words and Music: T. Harris

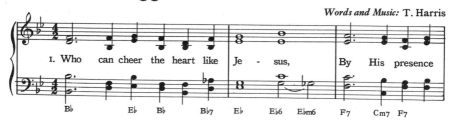

1. Who can cheer the heart like Je-sus, By His presence

2. Love of Christ so freely given,
    Grace of God beyond degree,
    Mercy higher than the heaven,
    Deeper than the deepest sea:
    Chorus

3. What a wonderful redemption!
    Never can a mortal know
    How my sin, tho'red like crimson,
    Can be whiter than the snow:
    Chorus

4. Ev'ry need His hand supplying,
    Ev'ry good in Him I see;
    On His strength divine relying,
    He is all in all to me:
    Chorus

5. By the crystal flowing river
    With the ransom'd I will sing,
    And for ever and for ever
    Praise and glorify the King:
    Chorus

56. Things are different now

Words and Music: S.W. Gavitt

(Low voices)

Things are diff'rent now, something happened to me When I gave my heart to

F   Bb   F   C7

(High voices)

Je - sus. Things are dif - f'rent now; I was chang'd, it must be, When I
(unison D.S.) Things are dif - f'rent now: something happened that day When I

F   Bb   F

Fine

gave my heart to Him.——
gave my heart to Him.——

Unison
Things I loved be - fore have

C7   F   Bb

D.S.al Fine

passed a - way, Things I love far more have come to stay.

F   G9   G7   C7

57. It's an open secret

Words and Music: J. Webb

— It's an o - pen se - cret, I love my Sa - viour so. —
know; Se - cret, O I love Him so.
Em G D7 G
And you can seek Him, find Him, Share this se - cret,
C G G°
too; Know His lov - ing kind - ness in ev - 'ry - thing you
G Em Bm Em A7

58. No one ever cared for me like Jesus

Words and music: C. F. Weigle

oth - er friend so kind as He; No one
else could take the sin and dark - ness from me
O how much He cared for me.

2.   All my life was full of sin when Jesus found me,
     All my heart was full of misery and woe;
     Jesus placed His strong and loving arms about me,
     And He led me in the way I ought to go:
          Chorus

3.   Ev'ry day He comes to me with new assurance,
     More and more I understand His words of love;
     But I'll never know just why He came to save me
     Till some day I see His blessed face above:
          Chorus

59. He gives me satisfying peace

Words and Music: N. J. Clayton

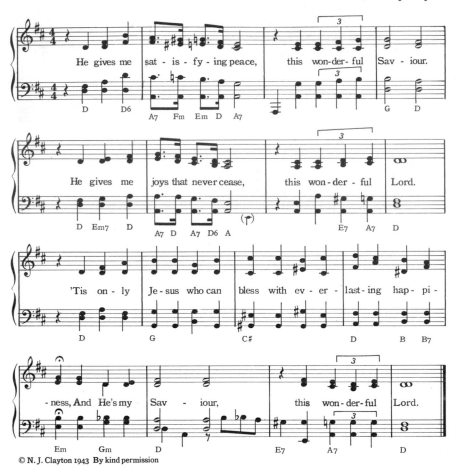

He gives me sat - is - fy - ing peace, this won-der-ful Sav - iour.

He gives me joys that never cease, this won-der - ful Lord.

'Tis on - ly Je - sus who can bless with ev - er - last-ing hap - pi -

- ness, And He's my Sav - iour, this won-der-ful Lord.

© N. J. Clayton 1943 By kind permission

60. Jesus is a wonderful Saviour

Traditional
arr. W.G. Hathaway

Je - sus is a won-der - ful Sav - iour, He will carry you thro',

Je - sus is a won-der-ful Sav - iour, He will car-ry you thro', my bro-ther;

Je - sus is a won-der-ful Sav - iour He will car-ry you thro', And when the

bat-tle is done And the victory's won, My Lord will carry you thro', And on that

last day When you're fac-ing your Mak - er, You'll need my

Je - sus To be your Sav - iour; He'll ev - er

hide you___ in the rock of a - ges,___ The rock of

F   C   G7   C

rit.   *pp*

a - ges___ that was cleft for you, that was cleft for you.

G   Dm7   G6   G7   C   F   Fm   C

61. Jesus is the Saviour

Words and Music: M. Wood
arr. G.R. Timms

Je - sus is the Saviour whom I love to know,

G   Dm7

Bass an octave lower and well marked.

Heaven is the haven that I'm going to___ Je - sus is the captain who now

G   G+   C

leads my life; Un - wor - thy as I am I know He came to save A

sin-ner such as me, a sin-ner such as me He came to save from the

Fine CHORUS

grave: For God so loved the world that He gave His

on - ly be-gotten Son That who - so - ever be -

- lieveth on Him should not per- ish But have ev - er last - ing life.

D

2.   Sometimes when you're feeling all alone and blue,
     Jesus can come in and help to pull you through;
     Sometimes you just know that you need Jesus too,
     So come on sinner, come to Him, He died for you
     A sinner such as you, a sinner such as me
     He came to save from the grave:
              Chorus

3.   Jesus is the Saviour whom I love to know,
     Heaven is the haven where I'm going to go;
     Jesus is the captain who now leads my life,
     Unworthy as I am I know He came to save
     A sinner such as me, a sinner such as me
     He came to save from the grave:

62. Walking in the King's highway

Words: B.D. Ackley
Music: A.H. Ackley

Days are filled with glad-ness, nights are filled with song,_ Walking in the King's high -

D   Em   A   A7   (The

-way (High - way___) And the world grows brighter, as we pass a long,_

King high - way I'm walking) D   Em

D   C°   A7

Walking in the King's high-way. Walking, walk-ing in the King's high - way,
(Yes I'm)

A A7 D   C° A7 C° A7

Walking in the King's high - way,   To the place of man-y mansions
(The King's highway)

A7   D

I shall come at last,____ Walking in the King's high - way.

Em   A7   D

2. Music from the homeland fills me with delight,
   Walking in the King's highway;
   Visions of the glory break upon my sight,
   Walking in the King's highway.
   Chorus

3. Crowned with tender mercies, guarded by His love,
   Walking in the King's highway;
   Jesus gives a foretaste of the joys above,
   Walking in the King's highway.
   Chorus

63. The King of Love

Words: Sir H.W. Baker
Music: The Followers
arr. D.G. Wilson

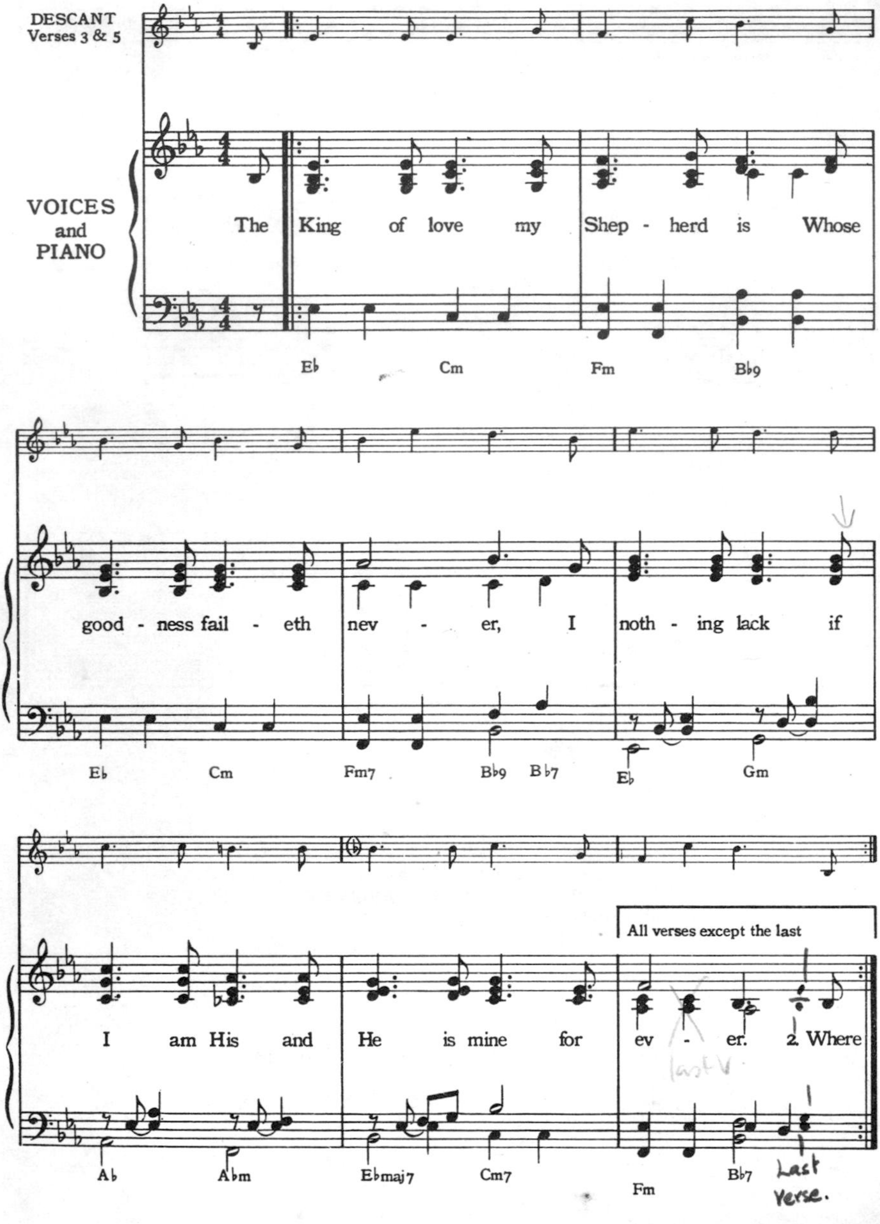
DESCANT
Verses 3 & 5
VOICES
and
PIANO
The King of love my Shep - herd is Whose
Eb Cm Fm Bb9
good - ness fail - eth nev - er, I noth - ing lack if
Eb Cm Fm7 Bb9 Bb7 Eb Gm
I am His and He is mine for ev - er. 2. Where
All verses except the last
Ab Abm Ebmaj7 Cm7 Fm Bb7
Last Verse.

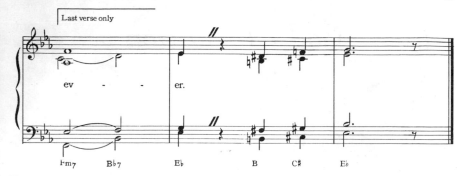

Last verse only

ev - - er.

Fm7   Bb7   Eb   B   C#   Eb

3 Verses.

2. Where streams of living water flow
   My ransomed soul He leadeth,
   And where the verdant pastures grow
   With food celestial feedeth.

4. In death's dark vale I fear no ill
   With Thee, dear Lord, beside me;
   Thy rod and staff my comfort still,
   Thy cross before to guide me.

3. Perverse and foolish oft I strayed,
   But yet in love He sought me
   And on His shoulder gently laid
   And home, rejoicing, brought me.

5. Thou spread'st a table in my sight;
   Thy unction grace bestoweth;
   And O, what transport of delight
   From Thy pure chalice floweth!

6. And so through all the length of days
   Thy goodness faileth never;
   Good Shepherd, may I sing Thy praise
   Within Thy house for ever.

GUITARISTS suggested $\frac{12}{8}$ rhythm.

VOICES

GUITAR RHYTHM

F

God's Invitation

64. Rise up and walk

Words and Music: G.R. Timms

Rise up and walk! All pow'r is giv-en un-to Him, He

chan-ges not, and sin shall not have vic-t'ry ov-er you.

Rise up and walk! He is the Lord that heal-eth thee, At

His command thou shalt be free, Christ Je-sus makes you whole!

65. There is full salvation

Words: **M.A. Baughen**
Music: **N.L. Warren**

2. He gives fellowship and guidance all the way:
   As we pray— ev'ry day;
   He gives fellowship and guidance all the way:
   There is no friend like Jesus.

3. Death is swallowed up for all eternity:
   Death will be— victory!
   Death is swallowed up for all eternity:
   We trust a risen Jesus.

4. There is full salvation through that precious Name:
   Jesus came— took our blame;
   There is full salvation through that precious Name:
   No other name like Jesus.

66. Ho! everyone

Words and Music: M.A. Baughen

Ho! ev-'ryone that thirsts in life Hear the off - er of the Lord;

He is the one who sat - is - fies— Come of__ your own ac-cord.

Let the wick-ed for-sake his way And the un-righteous his thoughts;

Let him return to the Lord our God And he will find pardon and mer - cy— a-

- bundant-ly! Seek ye the Lord while He may be found, Call on Him while He's

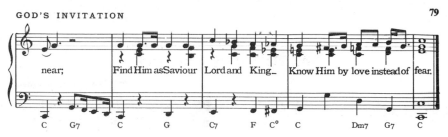

near; Find Him as Saviour Lord and King_ Know Him by love instead of fear.

67. Behold I stand

Words and Music: C. Blissard-Barnes

Moderato

p Be - hold I stand, I stand at the door and knock, Be-

- hold I stand at the door and knock; If an - y

man will hear_ my_ voice Let him o - pen the door_ and_

mf *poco rit* *pp*

I will come in and sup with him and_ he with me.

68. Behold I stand

Words and Music: M.A. Baughen

is the promise of His Word and it is true. When

F♯ Bm Bm7 E7 A7 *D.S.*

When He comes in it's fellowship divine,
For I am His and He is mine;
When He comes in, then He will sup with me
Until that day His face I'll see.

This is the invitation that Jesus gives to you,
This is the promise of His Word and it is true.

Behold He stands, He stands at the door and knocks,
Behold He stands, He stands at the door and knocks;
If any man will listen to His voice, and open that door—
He will come in.

69. There's a way back to God

Words and Music: E.H. Swinstead

There's a way back to God from the dark paths of sin; There's a

D7 G G° G D D7 G F♯ F♯7 D7

door that is o-pen and you may go in: At Cal-va-ry's cross is

G Em Bm Em Am A9 D D7 G G° G

where you be-gin, When you come as a sin-ner to Je - sus.

G Dm G7 C G° G C G D7 G

70. I heard the voice of Jesus

Words: H. Bonar
Music: N.L. Warren

glad.___

F   B♭   F   C₇   C   G₉   C₇   F   F6

2. I heard the voice of Jesus say,
    'Behold, I freely give
    The living water: thirsty one,
    Stoop down and drink, and live.'
    I came to Jesus and I drank
    Of that life-giving stream;
    My thirst was quenched, my soul revived,
    And now I live in Him.

3. I heard the voice of Jesus say,
    'I am this dark world's light,
    Look unto me, thy morn shall rise,
    And all thy days be bright.'
    I looked to Jesus and I found
    In Him my star, my sun;
    And in that light of life I'll walk,
    Till travelling days are done.

71. Get on the road

Words: M.A. Baughen
Music: N.L. Warren

(To be sung to the tune of No. 70)

1. Broad is the way that leads man to
    The place that's called destruction;
    Narrow the way to life anew,
    The way which few will walk on:

Chorus Get on the road which leads you to God
          Start at the cross of Jesus;
          He is the way, the truth, and the life-
          So trust Him, come and follow Jesus (Jesus).

2. God has prepared a place for all
    Who trust in Christ as Saviour;
    His promise is that at His call
    We'll live with Him for ever:
                                    Chorus

3. We can draw near to God in prayer,
    Know Him as Friend and Father;
    We can approach God without fear,
    And know His love forever:
                                    Chorus

4. No other way to God is true,
    No other way than Jesus,
    No other way to God for you-
    Jesus alone can save us:
                                    Chorus

72. If you want joy

Words and Music: arr. W.G. Hathaway

If you want joy, real joy, won-der-ful joy, let Jesus come in-to your heart. If you want joy, real joy, won-der-ful joy, let Je-sus come in to your heart. Your sins He'll take a-way, your night He'll turn to day. Your heart He'll make o-ver a-new, and then come in to stay. If you want joy, real

joy, won-der-ful joy, let Je-sus come in-to your heart.

Dm Gm C7 F Gm F C7 F C7 F

73. Jesus is knocking

Words and Music G. Brattle

Je-sus is knock-ing, pa-tient-ly wait-ing, Out-side your

F Dm Gm C Dm Dm7

heart's closed door.___ Do not re-ject Him, sim-ply ac-

G9 G7 C C7 F Dm Gm

-cept Him, Now and for-ev-er-more.___

A9 A7 Gm7 F C7 F

74. In Christ there is full salvation

Words and Music: A.E. Kelly

Challenge

75. Take up the cross

Words: R. J.B Eddison
Music: G.E.F. Rawlins

76. Make up your mind

Words and Music: R.T. Bewes
arr. M.C.T. Strover

Which way are you choosing, the nar-row or broad? You'll have to make up your mind._____ Just give up your own way and fol-low the Lord; Why don't you make up your mind?_____ He died, the strang-er of Ga-li-lee, to bring sal-va-tion to you and me; A strong com-pan-ion you'll prove Him to be, So won't you make up your mind?____

2. Which crowd will you follow, the large or the small?
Be sure to make up your mind.
The cost is demanding, but hear Jesus call;
Then come and make up your mind.
Your friends may shun you unthinkingly,
But Christ gives power and liberty;
To life with purpose you'll find the key,
When once you make up your mind!

3. On which are you resting, the Rock or the sand?
You'd better make up your mind!
With Christ as foundation your building will stand,
But have you made up your mind?
Temptations and trials must come your way,
The storms of Judgement will rage one day;
Take Jesus and on Him your confidence stay,
Don't wait, but make up your mind!

4. O what will you do with the Saviour today?
He bids you make up your mind.
Repent and accept Him without delay,
O sinner, make up your mind!
Why stumble alone along the road?
He'll sort your tangles, He'll take your load,
And in your heart He will make his abode;
It's time to make up your mind!

77. You'd better get on that road

Words and Music: M.C. Dunlop

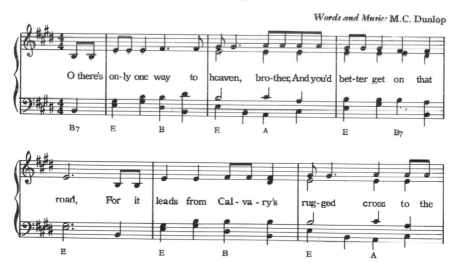

gates of the ci - ty of God. For oth - er roads will

E B7 E A

lead a - stray, So take the strait and nar - row way; And you'd

E F#m B E F#7 B B7

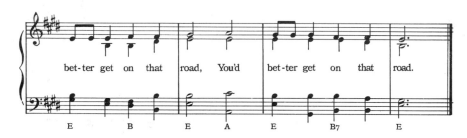

bet-ter get on that road, You'd bet-ter get on that road.

E B E A E B7 E

2. O there's only one way to heaven, brother,
And you'd better get on that road;
For salvation's free, not by works you see,
It is the gift of God's love bestowed.
Your sin on Christ was fully laid,
Its penalty is really paid;
So you'd better get on that road,
You'd better get on that road.

3. O there's only one way to heaven, brother,
And you'd better get on that road;
For Christ is the door, and His word is the key
To a home in that blest abode.
He is the Truth, the Life, the Way,
O trust Him now without delay;
And you'd better get on that road;
You'd better get on that road.

78. How long

Words and Music: M. Wood
arr. G.R. Timms

you and me; But still you go on living that way: Come on now, come

.under His sway. So come a - long, you'll sing that new

song, to - day To Jesus come a - long___

79. Christian are you running

Words: H.V. Davies
Music: D.G. Wilson

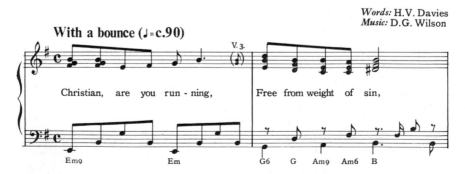

With a bounce (♩=c.90)

Christian, are you run - ning, Free from weight of sin,

With the hope be-fore you A crown of life to win?

Or is your bur-den heav-y, Each step like backward pace:

How are you pro-gress-ing In the Christian race?

2. Where as you are running
   Do you fix your eyes,
   Are they set on Jesus
   With faith that never dies?
   Or is your vision dazzled
   With idols on the way:
   How are you progressing
   In the race today?

3. Are you ever mindful
   Of watchers yet unseen,
   Saints of God before you
   Who in the race have been?
   Or are your thoughts still dwelling
   On things the world holds dear:
   How are you progressing—
   Keep the vision clear.

4. Christian, press thou onwards,
   Looking to the Lord,
   Think now how His life-blood
   Was for thy soul outpoured;
   Then leave all burdens with Him,
   O never drag that load,
   End the race rejoicing,
   In that blest abode.

80. The Jericho road

Words and Music: D.S. McCrossan
arr. L.G. Presley

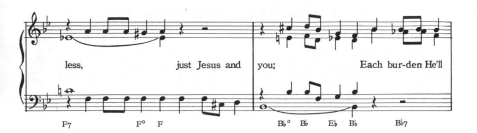

less,   just Jesus and   you;   Each bur-den He'll

F7   F° F   B♭° B♭   E♭ B♭   B♭7

bear,_____   each sor- row He'll share,_____   There's nev-er a

E♭   E♭° E♭6 E♭   B♭

care,_____ _____   for Je - sus is there._____

F7   F°   F7   B♭7   B♭°   E♭m B♭

2. On the Jericho road blind Bartimaeus sat,
    His life was a void, so empty and flat;
    But Jesus appeared, one word brought him sight,
    On the Jericho road, Christ banished his night.

3. O brother, to you this message I bring,
    Though hope may be gone, He'll cause you to sing;
    At Jesus' command sin's shackles must fall,
    On the Jericho road, will you answer His call?

81. If any man will follow

Words and Music: **M.A. Baughen**

world ... And then ... los-es ... his ... soul! ...
day ... When in ... glo-ry ... He ... comes! ...

F　Dm7　G7　　　　C7　　　　　D.C.

Let ... him ... come ... and ... fol-low ... af-ter ... my ... Lord!__

Dm　F　G9　Bbm7　Abm　Dm7　Cm7　C7　F

1. If any man will follow, if any man will follow,
If any man will follow after my Jesus:
Let him deny himself, oh, let him take up his cross,
And let him come and follow after my Lord!

　　Whosoever will live for self will throw his life away,
　　Christ gives life to all who follow Him—
　　What is a man advantaged if he gains the whole wide world
　　And then loses his soul!

2. If any man will follow, if any man will follow,
If any man will follow after my Jesus:
Let him deny himself, oh, let him take up his cross,
And let him come and follow after my Lord!

　　Whosoever will be ashamed of Jesus and His words,
　　In this sinful age in which we live,
　　Jesus the King will be ashamed of him in that great day,
　　When in glory He comes!

3. If any man will follow, if any man will follow,
If any man will follow after my Jesus,
Let him deny himself, oh, let him take up his cross,
And let him come and follow after my Lord!
Let Him come and follow after my Lord

82. I'm glad I'm a Christian

Words: verses 1 & 2 Anon.
verses 3 & 4 A. Boddington
Music: arr. G.R. Timms

I'm glad I'm a Christ - ian,____ I'm trust-ing the Lord;____

____ I rest on God's prom - ise____ Be-lieving His Word.

2. The past is forgiven,
And now I am free;
A mansion in heaven
Is waiting for me.

3. O come to Jesus,
Your sins all confess;
He's longing to clothe you
In His righteousness.

4. Admit you're a sinner,
Believe He is true;
And when you have found Him
Your life He'll renew.

83. They are watching you

Words: R.T. Bewes
Music: R.T. Bewes
arr. M.C.T. Strover

1. Though the world has for - sa - ken God, Treads a diff -'rent path, lives a

diff-'rent way, I walk the road that the Sav-iour trod, And all may

know I live un-der Je-sus' sway: They are watch-ing you,— mark-ing

all you do, Hear-ing the things— you say; Let them

see the Saviour as He shines in you, Let His pow'r con-trol you ev-'ry day.

2. Men will look at the life I lead,
See the side I take, and the things I love;
They judge my Lord by my every deed—
Lord, set my affections on things above:
Chorus

3. When assailed in temptation's hour,
By besetting sins, by the fear of man,
Then I can know Jesus' mighty power,
And become like Him in His perfect plan:
Chorus

4. Here on earth people walk in night;
With no lamp to guide, they are dead in sin;
I know the Lord Who can give them light,
I live, yet not I, but Christ within:
Chorus

84. If you will follow Jesus

Words and Music: J.B. Hindley
arr. W. Wooldridge

85. God cares for you

Words and Music: M. Wood
arr. G.R. Timms

There's a time   when you tra - vel   way back in   time;

When you try,   to un - rav - el,   and up - wards climb:

Up a-bove the sor-rows and scares, In search of

someone who cares, And you find that God cares for you: He'll see you

through; If you think and pray, Simply trust and say, Come___

_ and make my life be new.

2. The place your search leads you to has no escape;
   Up a hill to a cross it's true— a grim landscape:
   Calvary's the place you're in,
   Christ is dying for your sin,
   And you know that God cares for you. . .

3. Come with me up to His side and see His face;
   Kneel awhile, forget your pride and see His grace:
   Hear Him say "Forgive them all",
   Now listen to His call,
   And you'll find that God cares for you. . .

4. It is hard for you to understand, but try you must;
   As a child takes his father's hand you must have trust:
   Trust in Christ— He died for you,—
   Believe in this- you know it's true,
   That God cares for you . . .

Prayer and the Bible

86. Never doubt the Word

Words and Music: R. McCurdy Jones

Lyrics (verse): Not one pre - cious prom - ise of His Word Ev - er failed the ser - vants of the Lord, Tried and proved by many like fine gold, Sweeter than the hon - ey - comb:

CHORUS: Nev - er doubt the Word, God's own prec - ious Word, Nev - er doubt the Word of God. There's a

prom-ise true In the Book for you, Nev-er doubt the Word of God.

C   F   C   D7   G7   C

2. Ev'ryone who takes God at His Word
Need by doubters never be deterred,
He will find the promise, read or heard,
Never failing to be true:
Chorus:

3. Ev'ry promise can be yours or mine
As to Him our minds in prayer incline,
If our hearts have known His love divine
We will want to love Him more:
Chorus:

© R. McCurdy Jones 1964 By kind permission

87. All Scriptures

Words and Music: M.A. Baughen
arr. W. Wooldridge

All Scriptures are given by the breath of God, Are in-spired of God, Are the

C7   F   Gm7   F   Bb   Bb6   C7

Word of the Lord; All Scriptures are given by the breath of God, And

F   C   C7   F   Bbm   F   F6   F+

Fine

glor - i - fy His Name! They can make you wise to a

C7   F   C   F

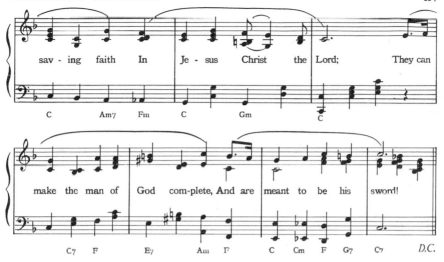

sav - ing faith In Je - sus Christ the Lord; They can

C Am7 Fm C Gm C

make the man of God com-plete, And are meant to be his sword!

C7 F E7 Am F C Cm F G7 C7 *D.C.*

1. All Scriptures are given by the breath of God,
   Are inspired of God,
   Are the Word of the Lord;
   All Scriptures are given by the breath of God,
   And glorify His Name!

   They can make you wise to a saving faith
   In Jesus Christ the Lord;
   They can make the man of God complete,
   And are meant to be His sword!

2. So study to show yourself approved to God,
   Fit to use His Word,
   Fit to speak in His Name;
   So study to show yourself approved to God,
   A workman not ashamed.

   They'll reprove, correct, and a training in
   All righteous living afford;
   They will yield up all that we need to know
   Of the teaching of the Lord!

3. All Scriptures are given by the breath of God,
   Are inspired of God,
   Are the Word of the Lord;
   All Scriptures are given by the breath of God,
   And glorify His Name!

H

88. Before you start the day

Words: M.A. Baughen
Music: R. McCurdy Jones

Be-fore you start the day__ Take time a-lone to pray, And feed up-on God's Word To know His way;__ So start the day with Him,__Then walk the way with Him__ and come to eve-ning time with praise to Him__

© M.A. Baughen and R. McCurdy Jones 1964 By kind permission

89. Lord who left the highest heaven

Words: T. Dudley-Smith
Music: M.A. Baughen

1. Lord, who left the highest heav-en For a homeless human birth, And, a child within a sta-ble, Came to

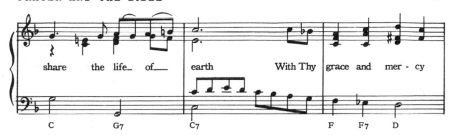

2. Lord, who sought by cloak of darkness
   Refuge under foreign skies
   From the swords of Herod's soldiers,
   Ravaged homes, and parents' cries—
   May Thy grace and mercy rest
   On the homeless and oppressed.

4. Lord, who leaving home and kindred,
   Followed still as duty led,
   Sky the roof and earth the pillow
   For the Prince of Glory's head—
   With Thy grace and mercy bless
   Sacrifice for righteousness

3. Lord, who lived secure and settled,
   Safe within the Father's plan,
   And in wisdom, stature, favour
   Growing up from boy to man—
   May Thy grace and mercy bless
   Us with growth in holiness.

5. Lord, who in Thy Cross and Passion
   Helpless hung 'twixt earth and sky,
   Yet whose thoughts were for Thy mother,
   And a thief condemned to die—
   May Thy grace and mercy rest
   On the helpless and distressed.

6. Lord, who rose to life triumphant
   With man's whole salvation won,
   Risen, glorified, ascended,
   All Thy Father's purpose done—
   May Thy grace, all conflict past,
   Bring Thy children home at last.

90. All your anxiety

Words and Music: E.H. Joy

All your anx-i-e-ty, all your care, Bring to the mer-cy-seat, leave it there.

Ne-ver a bur-den He can-not bear, Ne-ver a friend like Je- -sus.

© The Salvation Army International Music Board By kind permission

91. O Lord, teach me to pray

Words and Music: Pfarrer Julius
tr. S. Lonsdale and M.A. Baughen

♩ = 100

O Lord, teach me to pray,—

As I be-lieve on You.—

O Lord, teach me to pray,—

92. God answers prayer

Words: F. Wallingford
Music: D.M. Allen

God hears and He an-swers pray'r; Cast on Jesus your
ev-'ry care, Trust in His prom-is-es, they can-not fail,
For with the Fa-ther He'll ev-er pre-vail. God hears and He
an-swers pray'r, Frees my spir-it from all des-pair;
Hasten to take Him your problems, For God an-swers prayer.

Strength in the Lord

93. Trust in the Lord

Words and Music: R. McCurdy Jones

2. Trust in the Lord, and not in any fable,
   Trust in the Lord, and find Him wholly true,
   Trust in the Lord, and know that He is able
   To fill your whole life through.

3. Trust in the Lord, and not in men or nation,
   Trust in the Lord, as Saviour, Lord, and King,
   Trust in the Lord for full and free salvation,
   And lift your heart and sing.

4. Trust in the Lord, faith is a great adventure,
   Trust in the Lord, and never cease to pray,
   Trust in the Lord, for all the unknown future,
   Today and every day!

94. God's will for you

Words and Music: M.G. Schneider
tr. and adapted S. Lonsdale and M.A. Baughen

1. God's will for you is good,
In the pattern of life
What - so - ever each day may bring:
Sing Him your song.

2. God's will for you is good,
Ev'ry morning anew
Think upon His great faithfulness:
Sing Him your song.

3. God's will for you is good,
Stop to ponder again
All the blessings and gifts He gives:
Sing Him your song.

4. God's will for you is good,
Even sorrow and pain
Can bring blessing through His grace:
Sing Him your song.

5. God's will for you is good,
For He sent His own Son
To bear all our guilt and sin:
Sing Him your song.

6. God's will for you is good,
Be it sorrow or joy
He is faithful in life and death:
Sing Him your song.

95. I can do all things

Words and Music: M.A. Baughen

With a swing - fairly fast

1. I can do all things through Christ the Lord who strengthens me; I can do all things Through Jesus Christ my King.___ For He is the strength of my heart and my soul, O Jesus, my Sav - i - our; And He is my friend and my Lord and my all, O Jesus, my Lord.

2. I can do all things
Through Christ my Lord who strengthens me;
I can do all things
Through Jesus Christ my King.
I'm kept by the pow'r of His sheltering hand,
O Jesus, my Saviour;
He'll bring me at last to that heavenly land
O Jesus, my Lord.

3. I can do all things
Through Christ my Lord who strengthens me;
I can do all things
Through Jesus Christ, my King!

96. When the road is rough

Words and Music: N. J. Clayton

When the road is rough and steep, Fix your eyes up-on Je - sus,

He a - lone has pow'r to keep, Fix your eyes up- on Him;

Je - sus is a gracious friend, One on whom you can de - pend,

He is faith - ful to the end, Fix your eyes up-on Him.

97. Christ be my leader

Words: T. Dudley-Smith
Music: M. A. Baughen
arr. C. Roberts

1. Christ be my lead - er____ By night as by day;____

Safe through the | dark - ness,___ | For He is the | Way.___

Bb

V.3

Nor 'darkness nor'

Fears for the | fu - ture___ | I trust to His | care;___

E°   Bb   Bb7   Eb

V.3

Can touch my Sal-'

Dark - ness is | day - light___ | When Jesus is | there.___

F#°   F7   Bb

2. Christ be my teacher
   In age as in youth,
   Drifting or doubting,
   For He is the Truth.
   Grant me to trust Him;
   Though shifting as sand,,
   Doubt cannot daunt me:
   In Jesus I stand.

3. Christ be my saviour
   In calm as in strife;
   Death cannot hold me
   For He is the life.
   Nor darkness nor doubting,
   Nor sin and it's stain,
   Can touch my Salvation:
   With Jesus I reign.

98. When Jesus comes to you

Words and Music: J. Webb

Slow, relaxed rhythm ♩=104

Fellows (melody)
When Je - sus comes to you He'll bring {1. glad - ness,
{2. com - fort,

Girls
1. glad -
2. com -

- ness,   He'll bring (peace;
- fort,   He'll bring (light;

When Je - sus comes to you He'll bring

you   He'll   fill   your   heart   with   glad - ness,   You'll   make

others   hap - py   too;   fill   your   heart   with   glad - ness,   When

Je - sus   Je - sus   comes   to   you.

99. Christ is the answer

Words and Music: T.W. Maltby

Christ___ is the an - swer to my ev - 'ry need;

D   G   D   Em   B   Em

Christ___ is the an - swer, He is my friend in - deed.___

A7   D   A7   D   F#m7

Prob - lems of life my spi - rit may as - sail,___

Bm   F#   G   Em6   D   D9

With Christ my Sav - iour I need nev - er fail, For

G   A7   D   Bm   E9   E7   A   A7

Christ___ is the an - swer to my need.

D   G   D   Em7   A   D

100. When I have sorrow

Words and Music: H.H. Lemmel

1. When I have sorrow in my heart, What can take it a - way?
2. When I have fear_ in my heart, What can take it a - way?
3. When I have sin_ in my heart, What can take it a - way?

On - ly Je - sus in my heart Can take that sorrow a - way.
On - ly Je - sus in my heart Can take that fear_ a - way.
On - ly Je - sus in my heart Can take that sin_ a - way.

4. When I have Je - sus in my heart,_ What can take Him a - way?

More slowly, and with emphasis

Once take Je - sus in - to my heart, And He has come_ to stay.

© H.H. Lemmel and National Sunday School Union By kind permission

101. Just a closer walk

Traditional
arr. M.C.T. Strover

* These more simple chords can be used when accompaniment is by guitar only.

Chorus: Just a closer walk with Thee,
Grant it, Jesus, this my plea,
Daily walking close with Thee,
Let it be, dear Lord, let it be.

2. Through this world of toils and snares,
If I falter, Lord, who cares?
Who with me my burden shares?
None but Thee, dear Lord, none but Thee:
   Chorus

3. When my feeble life is o'er,
Time for me will be no more,
Guide me gently, safely home,
To Thy Kingdom's shore, to Thy shore:
   Chorus

I

102. I know who holds the future

Words and Music: A.B. Smith and E. Clark

trust the God of mir - a - cles, Give to Him my all.

C   Eb7   G   G7   E7   G°   Em   A7   D7   G

2. I do not know how many days
Of life are mine to spend;
But one who knows and cares for me
Will keep me to the end:
Chorus:

3. I do not know the course ahead,
What joys and griefs are there;
But one is near who fully knows,
I'll trust His loving care:
Chorus:

103. We'll understand it better by and by

Traditional
arr. M.C.T. Strover

CHORUS

By and by_____ when the morning comes And

G   C   G

all the saints of God are gathering home, We will

G   A   D   G

2. Temptations, hidden snares, often take us unawares
   And our hearts are made to bleed
   For each thoughtless word and deed;
   And we wonder why the test
   When we've tried to do our best,
   But we'll understand it better by and by:
   Chorus:

104. Burdens are lifted at Calvary

Words and Music: J.M. Moore

1. Days are filled with sorrow and care, Hearts are lonely and drear; Burdens are lif - ted at Cal - va - ry, Je - sus is ve - ry near. (ve - ry near)

CHORUS

Burdens are lif - ted at Cal - va - ry, Cal - va - ry,____ Cal - va - ry;____ Burdens are lif - ted at Cal - va - ry, Je - sus is ve - ry near.____ (ve - ry near)

2. Cast your care on Jesus today,
    Leave your worry and care;
    Burdens are lifted at Calvary,
    Jesus is very near:

    Chorus

3. Troubled soul, the Saviour can see,
    Ev'ry heartache and tear;
    Burdens are lifted at Calvary,
    Jesus is very near:

    Chorus

Dedication

105. Only to be

Words and Music: N. J. Clayton

On- ly to be what He wants me to be, Ev-'ry mo - ment of ev - 'ry day;

Yielded completely to Je - sus a-lone, Ev'ry step of this pil - grim way;

Just to be clay in the pot - ter's hands, Ready to do what His word commands,

On - ly to be what He wants me to be, Ev-'ry mo- ment of ev - 'ry day.

106. Cleanse me

Words and Music: R. Hudson Pope

Cleanse me from my sin, Lord, Put Thy pow'r with-in, Lord, Take me as I

am, Lord, And make me all Thine own;— Keep me day by day, Lord,

Underneath Thy sway, Lord, Make my heart Thy palace and Thy roy - al throne.

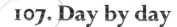

107. Day by day

Words: Richard of Chichester
Music: D. Austin

Day by day, dear Lord, of Thee three things I

pray: To see Thee more clear - ly, To love Thee more

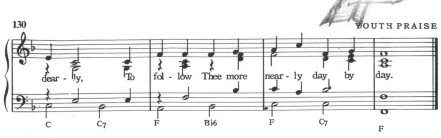

dear - ly, To fol - low Thee more near - ly day by day.

C   C₇   F   B♭6   F   C₇   F

© D. Austin 1964 By kind permission

108. Spirit of the living God

Words and Music: arr. W.G. Hathaway

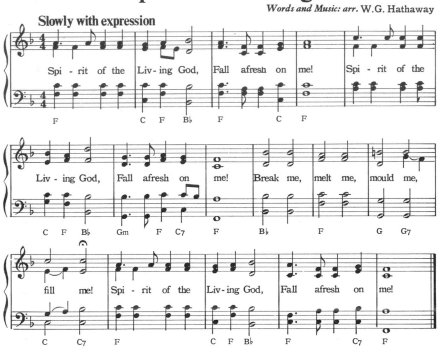

Slowly with expression

Spi - rit of the Liv - ing God, Fall afresh on me! Spi - rit of the

F   C F B♭   F   C F

Liv - ing God, Fall afresh on me! Break me, melt me, mould me,

C F B♭   Gm   F C₇   F   B♭   F   G   G₇

fill me! Spi - rit of the Liv - ing God, Fall afresh on me!

C   C₇   F   C F B♭   F   C₇   F

© The Victory Press Ltd. By kind permission

109. I'll be a friend to Jesus

Words: J. Oatman
Music: J.W. Dennis
arr. G.R. Timms

1. They tried my Lord and Master, With no one to de -
   (*my Lord*)

E♭   B♭ E♭   B♭   E♭   Cm B♭   E♭   F₇

2. The world may turn against Him,
I'll love Him to the end;
And while on earth I'm living,
My Lord shall have a friend:
Chorus:

3. I'll do what He may bid me,
I'll go where He may send;
I'll try each flying moment
To prove that I'm His friend:
Chorus:

4. To all who need a saviour,
My friend I recommend;
Because He brought salvation
Is why I am His friend:
Chorus:

110. Bring forth the fruit

Words and Music: **M.A. Baughen**
arr. **W. Wooldridge**

Bring forth the fruit of the Spir-it in your life,_____ Let the
life of Christ be seen in you;__ Bring forth the
fruit of the Spir-it in your life,_____ And let the
Lord be glorified____ in you._____ Seek His
pa - tience____ and His kind - ness,____ Seek His

F7 B♭ F7 B♭ C C7 F7 B♭ F D Gm7 C#° B♭ C7 F7 F+ B♭6

Fine

Start with chorus

Chorus   Bring forth the fruit of the Spirit in your life,
Let the life of Christ be seen in you;
Bring forth the fruit of the Spirit in your life,
And let the Lord be glorified in you.

1.   Seek His patience and His kindness,
Seek His gentleness and self-control,
Seek His goodness and His faithfulness,
And seek most His peace, and joy, and love:

Chorus   Bring forth the fruit of the Spirit in your life,
Let the life of Christ be seen in you;
Bring forth the fruit of the Spirit in your life,
And let the Lord be glorified in you.

III. As You cleanse me

Words and Music: O.G. Blarr
tr. S. Lonsdale and adapted by M.A. Baughen

1. As You cleanse me for to-day And for-give my yes-ter-day, As You cleanse me for to-day

12 & 3

I be-gin a - new, Lord. - new, Lord.

C+   Dm   C₇   F6   C₇   F   B♭m

I be-gin a - new, Lord.

F   C+   Dm   Gm7   G♭7   F6

2. As You've set me in this place
And sufficient is Your grace,
As You've set me in this place
I begin anew, Lord.

3. As You're watching over me
I can face the enemy,
As You're watching over me
I begin anew, Lord.

4. As I'm ever in Your sight
In the depth or in the height,
As I'm ever in Your sight
I begin anew, Lord.

112. O Holy Spirit, giver of life

Words: M. Saward
Music: P.C. Butler

O Ho - ly Spi - rit giv - er of life,

E♭   Cm   Fm7   B♭7

2. O Holy Spirit, giver of light,
   To minds where all is obscurity;
   Exchange for blindness, spiritual sight,
   That we may grow to maturity;
   Work out within us the Father's design,
   Give to us light, O Spirit Divine.

3. O Holy Spirit, giver of love,
   And joy, and peace, and fidelity;
   The fruitfulness which comes from above,
   That self-control and humility;
   Work out within us the Father's design,
   Give to us love, O Spirit Divine.

113. There is a place of quiet rest

Words and Music: C.B. McAfee

2. There is a place of comfort sweet,
Near to the heart of God,
A place where we our Saviour meet,
Near to the heart of God.
Chorus:

3. There is a place of full release,
Near to the heart of God,
A place where all is joy and peace,
Near to the heart of God:
Chorus:

114. According to the working

Words and Music: W. Wooldridge

Ac - cord-ing to the work-ing of His might-y pow'r We are
raised up to-geth - er with Christ. Ac -
-cord - ing to the plea - sure of his ho - ly will We are
washed and sanc - ti - fied. Ac - cording to the riches of His
glo - ry and His grace He sup - plies our ev - 'ry____

need. So that hence-forth we might live on - ly

un - to Him, Our__ friend and Lord in - deed.

115. Lord, make me useful

Words and Music: E.H.G. Sargent

Lord, make me use - ful to Thee,__

Send now Thy Spir - it to me,__ Thy per - fect will

In me ful - fil, Lord, make me use - ful to Thee.

K

116. His hands were pierced

Words and Music: D. Wood

1. His hands were pierced, the hands that made The moun - tain

F   F°   F   C₇

range and ev - er - glade; That washed the stains of

F   Dm₇   G₉   G₇   C   C₇   F   F°   C₇   F

sin___ a - way__ And changed earth's dark - ness in - to day.

F   F°   C₇   F   Gm   D°   F   Dm   Gm₇   C₇   F

2. His feet were pierced, the feet that trod
   The furthest shining star of God;
   And left their imprint deep and clear
   On ev'ry winding pathway here.

3. His heart was pierced, the heart that burned
   To comfort ev'ry heart that yearned;
   And from it came a cleansing flood,
   The river of redeeming blood.

4. His hands and feet and heart, all three
   Were pierced for me on Calvary;
   And here and now, to Him I bring,
   My hands, feet, heart, an offering.

117. I'll live for Jesus

Words and Music: P. J. Schultz

1. Though days are   long,___   oft filled with   care,___
2. Through ev - 'ry   day___   new joy I   find,___
   (though days are long)
   (through ev - ry day)

C   C°   C   C°
                                              G₇   (oft filled with
                                                      (new joy I

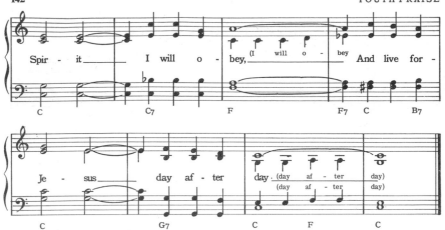

Spir - it___ I will o - bey, (I will o - bey) And live for -
C   C7   F   F7 C   B7

Je - sus___ day af - ter day. (day af - ter day)
C   G7   (day af - ter day)
                        C   F   C

118. Creator God

Words: Anon (Indian origin)
Music: N.L. Warren

1. Cre - a - tor God, Cre - a - tor God! With Thee
2. Cre - a - tor God, Cre - a - tor God! With Thy
3. And with Thy heart, Cre - a - tor God, I will

G   Em   C   D7   G   Em

Brighter

I am a man,___ But with - out Thee, O
hands may I work,___ With Thy feet may I
learn and love, ___ With Thy heart, O Cre -

Am   G   D7   G   C

Lord my Sav-iour, With-out Thee I am just a child.___
walk, O Sav-iour, And through Thine own eyes let me see.
a - tor God,_ I'll learn_ and love_ like Thee.

Am   D7   G   Am7 D7 G

119. I'll live for Christ

Words: M.A. Baughen
Music: R. McCurdy Jones

I'll live for Christ who gave Him-self on the tree I'm cru-ci-fied with Christ whose death set me free, And yet I live, for Christ is liv-ing in me: I'll live for Christ al-way, I'll live for Christ al-way, I'll serve Him ev-'ry day; I'll live by faith in Christ and trust in His grace I'll live for Christ al-way.

120. Sing Hosanna

Words: (version 1) A. Sevison
(others)
Music: arr. The Csehys

★ One group sustain 'Sing' while the other group does 'Sing Hosanna' etc.

Version 2

1. Give me joy in my heart, keep me praising,
   Give me joy in my heart, I pray;
   Give me joy in my heart, keep me praising,
   Keep me praising 'til the break of day:
   Chorus as version I

2. Give me peace in my heart, keep me resting . . .
   Chorus

3. Give me love in my heart, keep me serving . . .
   Chorus

Version 3

1. What a wonderful Saviour is Jesus,
   What a wonderful friend is He,
   For He left all the glory of heaven,
   Came to earth to die on Calvary:
   Chorus as version I

2. He arose from the grave, Hallelujah,
   And He lives never more to die,
   At the Father's right hand interceding
   He will hear and heed our faintest cry:
   Chorus

3. He is coming some day to receive us,
   We'll be caught up to heaven above,
   What a joy it will be to behold Him,
   Sing forever of His grace and love:
   Chorus

121. I want to walk

Words: St Paul's Erith 1964 Swiss Houseparty
Music: Swiss folk tune *(Es Buurebuebli)*
arr. C. Simmonds

To   give   to   Him___   com - plete   con -

G   D

trol   Of   bo - dy   and___   of   soul:___

A   A7
                         D   G   D

1. I want to walk with Jesus Christ,
    All the days I live of this life on earth,
    To give to Him complete control
    Of body and of soul:

Chorus   Follow Him, follow Him, yield your life to Him,
          He has conquered death, He is King of Kings,
          Accept the joy which He gives to those
          Who yield their lives to Him.

2. I want to learn to speak to Him,
    To pray to Him, confess my sin,
    To open my life and let Him in,
    For joy will then be mine:
                    Chorus

3. I want to learn to speak of Him,
    My life must show that He lives in me,
    My deeds, my thoughts, my words must speak
    All of His love for me:
                    Chorus

4. I want to learn to read His Word,
    For this is how I know the way
    To live my life as pleases Him,
    In holiness and joy:
                    Chorus

5. O Holy Spirit of the Lord,
    Enter now into this heart of mine,
    Take full control of my selfish will
    And make me wholly Thine:
                    Chorus

122. He'll understand and say "Well done"

Words: L.E. Campbell
Music: pop. *arr.* B. Gilbert
arr. G.R. Timms

1. O when you come to the end of life's journey,
Wear-y and worn, and the battle is done,
Carr-ying the Cross, the Cross of re-demption,
He'll un-der-stand and say 'Well done',
He'll un-der-stand and say 'Well done'.

2. Give, when you give, the best of your service,
Telling the world that the Saviour has come;
Be not dismayed if men won't defend you,
He'll understand and say "Well done",
He'll understand and say "Well done".

3. O when you try, and fail in your trying,
Hands sore and scarred from the work you have begun,
Come to the cross, come quickly to Jesus,
He'll understand and say "Well done",
He'll understand and say "Well done'.

123. Looking unto Jesus

Words: M.A. Baughen
Music: N.L. Warren

glo - ry, King for ev - er - more.

F   Dm7   Gm7   C7   F   Dm

2. Looking un - to   - more.

Gm7   C7   F   B♭6   F

3. Looking unto Jesus,
   In the Christian fight,
   Seeking grace to witness,
   Strengthened by His might,
   With the armour of Jesus,
   With the Spirit's sword,
   With much prayer that He'll bless His Word,
   Fighting for the Lord:
       Chorus

3. Looking unto Jesus
   Who despised the shame,
   Throwing off all hindrance
   As we bear His Name.
   Help us face all temptation,
   Lord, help us discern,
   Give us courage to speak for Thee
   Help our light to burn:
       Chorus

124. O Jesus, Lord and Saviour

Words: T.O. Chisholm
Music. C. Lowden

O Je-sus, Lord and Saviour, I give my-self to Thee; For Thou, in Thy a-

C7   F   C7   F   Gm   D7   Gm   C7

-tonement,Didst give Thy-self for me; I own no oth-er master, My heart shall

F   G7   C   F   C7   F   F7

rit.

be Thy throne; My life I give, hence-forth to live, O Christ, for Thee a-lone.

Bb   Bbm6   F   D7   G7   C7   F

125. I have decided

Words: Anon
Music: arr. C. Simmonds

1. I have de-ci-ded to fol-low Je-sus I have de-

D   A   D   D7

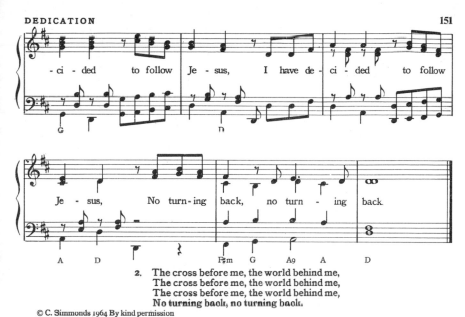

-ci-ded to follow Je-sus, I have de-ci-ded to follow

Je-sus, No turn-ing back, no turn-ing back.

2. The cross before me, the world behind me,
The cross before me, the world behind me,
The cross before me, the world behind me,
No turning back, no turning back.

126. Lord Jesus Christ

Words and Music: P. Appleford

1. Lord Je-sus Christ, You have come to us,

You are one with us, Ma - ry's Son. Cleansing our souls from

all their sin, Pouring your love and good-ness in, Je-sus, our love for

you   we   sing,   Liv - ing   Lord.   Lord.

D   B7   Em7   A7   D   Dm7   A7   D

At   2. Lord Jesus Christ,
Communion   Now and every day,
                        Teach us how to pray,
                            Son of God.
                        You have commanded us to do
                        This in remembrance, Lord, of You:
                        Into our lives Your power breaks through,
                            Living Lord.

                    3. Lord Jesus Christ,
                        You have come to us,
                        Born as one of us,
                            Mary's Son.
                        Led out to die on Calvary,
                        Risen from death to set us free,
                        Living Lord Jesus, help us see
                            You are Lord.

                    4. Lord Jesus Christ,
                        I would come to You,
                        Live my life for You,
                            Son of God.
                        All Your commands I know are true,
                        Your many gifts will make me new,
                        Into my life Your power breaks through,
                            Living Lord.

The Mission of the Church

127. Reigning Lord

Words: J.E. Seddon
Music: P. Appleford (as No. 126)

(To be sung to the tune of No. 126)

1. To Him we come:
   Jesus Christ our Lord,
   God's own living Word,
   His dear Son.
   In Him there is no east and west,
   In Him all nations shall be blest,
   To all He offers peace and rest,
   Loving Lord.

2. In Him we live:
   Christ our strength and stay,
   Life, and Truth, and Way,
   Friend divine.
   His power can break the chains of sin,
   Still all life's storms without, within,
   Help us the daily fight to win,
   Living Lord.

3. For Him we go
   Soldiers of the cross,
   Counting all things loss,
   Him to know;
   Going to men of every race,
   Preaching to all His wondrous grace,
   Building His Church in every place,
   Conquering Lord.

4. With Him we serve:
   His the work we share
   With saints everywhere,
   Near and far;
   One in the task which faith requires,
   One in the zeal which never tires,
   One in the hope His love inspires,
   Coming Lord.

5. Onward we go,
   Faithful, bold, and true,
   His blest will to do,
   Day by day.
   Till, at the last, with joy, we'll see
   Jesus, in glorious majesty;
   Live with Him through eternity,
   Reigning Lord!

128. Every person in every nation

Words and Music: Wycliffe Bible Translators

Deliberately (not too fast)

Ev - 'ry per - son in ev - 'ry nat - ion In each succeed - ing gen - er - a - tion

Db Ebm7 Db Db7   Ebm Bb Ebm Ab   Db Abᵢ Db Db7 Ebm Bb Ebm Ab7

Has the right to hear the news That Christ can save. Cru - ci - fied on

Db   Gb Db   Eb9 Eb7   Ab Ab7   Db Ebm7 Db Db7

Cal - v'ry's mountain He op-ened wide a cleansing foun-tain Con - quered sin and

Bbm Bb Ebm Ab   Db Ab7 Db Db7   Ebm Bb7 Ebm   Ab   Db   Gbm

Slower

death and hell, He rose up from the grave. Fa - ther, I am will - ing To

Db   Dbm   Eb7   Ab7 Db   A   Em A7   Db

ded - i - cate to Thee Life and ta-lent, time and mon-ey: Here am I send me.

Ab   Ab+ Db   Gb   Db Bbm6 F Bbm   Eb7   Ab7 Db

© Wycliffe Bible Translators By kind permission

129. A vessel called the Church of God

Words and Music: M.G. Schneider
tr. S. Lonsdale and adapted by M.A. Baughen

A vessel called the Church of God Sails ov - er time's great

sea: She sets her course for God's great port To

God's e - ter - ni - ty. The world at - tacks her

like a storm, There's dan - ger need, and fear; She

L

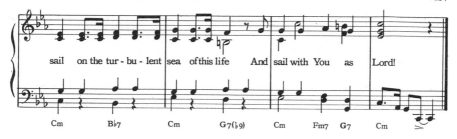

sail on the tur-bu-lent | sea of this life   And | sail with You   as | Lord!

Cm   Bb7   Cm   G7(b9)   Cm   Fm7   G7   Cm

2. What happens if the ship remains
   At moorings by the quay?
   What happens if she wants the calm
   And will not put to sea?
       It may be nice to glory in
       The vict'ries of the past,
       But God wants us to sail today—
       His colours at the mast!
   The course of God is sacrifice,
   We must not fear the cost;
   The life not lived for Christ the Lord
   Is life which God calls lost:
       Chorus

3. The ship we call the Church of God
   Depends upon its crew;
   There are no passengers aboard,
   There's work for all to do.
       God has a post for ev'ryone,
       A duty to fulfil;
       He gifted us, now looks to us,
       To do His perfect will.
   We work together as a team
   With fellowship in Him,
   We have a common faith and hope—
   The Spirit's power within:
       Chorus

4. The ship has many would-be guides
   Who state what course they think;
   They rest upon man's thought alone
   And with them we would sink!
       But God has made His course quite clear,
       His way is in His Word;
       We see the fulness of the truth
       As we look to the Lord.
   When onslaughts come upon our faith
   Let courage flood our hearts;
   We are a world-wide fellowship
   And share all God imparts:
       Chorus

130. There's a road

Words and Music: M.G. Schneider
tr. S. Lonsdale and adapted by M.A. Baughen

1. There's a road which leads from Je - ru - sa - lem, It's the
way down to Je - ri - cho, It's Com-passion road, steep and tir- ing road, Which has
dan-ger from thiev - ing foe. And here on this road is one man Beaten

up and left as half dead, Like many in this world a-round us Op-
-pressed, in des-pair or un-fed. Hear him cry out As he
lies on Compas-sion road.

2. Watch a priest and levite come down that road
Only giving the man small heed,
They are too caught up with religious thoughts
To give help to a man in need.
Samaritan, walk behind them!
You are not within the same class!
But you are the one who helps him—
You could not see need and just pass!
You heard the cry
As you walked on Compassion road.

3. The Compassion road goes right on through life,
It's a road with us still today,
Many hands are needed to give the help
To those stricken upon the way.
So now will you have compassion?
To the lonely, hungry, and worn,
To those without hope or salvation
To fearful and poor and forlorn?
Lord, give us grace
To give help on Compassion road.

131. The fields are white

Words and Music: M.A. Baughen

2. The harvest truly is fit to reap
But workers few,
The harvest truly is fit to reap
But workers few:
Chorus

3. Who else will 'go into all the world'
To preach the Word?
Who else will 'go into all the world'
To preach the Word?
Chorus

4. The Lord's return may be very soon,
The time is short!
The Lord's return may be very soon,
The time is short:
Chorus

132. Go forth and tell

Words: J.E. Seddon
Music: M.A. Baughen

With a swing

2. Go forth and tell! God's love embraces all:
He will in grace respond to all who call.
How shall they call if they have never heard
The gracious invitation of His Word?

3. Go forth and tell! Men still in darkness lie:
In wealth or want, in sin they live and die.
Give us, O Lord, concern of heart and mind,
A love like Thine which cares for all mankind.

4. Go forth and tell! The doors are open wide:
Share God's good gifts with men so long denied.
Live out your life as Christ, your Lord, shall choose,
Your ransomed powers for His sole glory use.

5. Go forth and tell! O Church of God, arise:
Go in the strength which Christ your Lord supplies.
Go, till all nations His great Name adore
And serve Him Lord and King for evermore.

The Heavenly Hope

133. O when the saints go marching in

Traditional *arr.* D.G. Wilson

O when the | saints _____ go marching | in, _____ O when the
(O when the saints) | (go march-ing in)

F

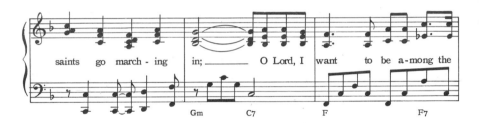

saints go march-ing | in; _____ O Lord, I | want to be a-mong the

Gm   C7   F   F7

num-ber_____ When the | saints go march-ing | in._____

B♭   Gm   Am7 B♭maj7 F6 C9   F

2. O when they crown Him Lord of all,
O when they crown Him Lord of all;
O Lord, I want to be among the number
When they crown Him Lord of all.

3. O when all knees bow at His name,
O when all knees bow at His name;
O Lord, I want to be among the number
When all knees bow at His name.

4. O when they sing the Saviour's praise,
O when they sing the Saviour's praise;
O Lord, I want to be among the number
When they sing the Saviour's praise.

5. O when the saints go marching in,
O when the saints go marching in;
O Lord, I want to be among the number
When the saints go marching in.

134. I gotta home

Traditional *arr.* M.C.T. Strover

Do Lord, oh, do Lord, oh, do re-mem-ber me;

G6   B7   Em7   A7

Way be - yond the blue.

G6   D9   G6   (C#b9   Gmaj7)

The verse accompaniment may be used for the chorus if the latter is found too hard.

2. I took Jesus as my Saviour,
   you take Him too . . . .

3. If you will not bear a cross,
   you can't wear a crown . . .

Alternative version

1. I gotta home in gloryland
      that outshines the sun,
   I gotta home in gloryland
      that outshines the sun,
   I gotta home in gloryland
      that outshines the sun,
   Way beyond the blue:

Chorus   Thank You, my Saviour, for that eternal life;
   Thank You, my Saviour, for that eternal life;
   Thank You, my Saviour, for that eternal life
   With You evermore!

2. Those who trust in Christ as Saviour
   shall never die. . .

3. If you will not bear a cross,
   you can't wear a crown. . .

© Copyright in this arrangement by M.C.T. Strover 1964 By kind permission

135. When I come

Words: T. Ramsey
Music: C.E. Durham

1. When I come to the riv-er at en-ding of day When the

last winds of sor-row have blown, There'll be some-bo-dy wait-ing to

show me the way, I won't have to cross Jor-dan a - lone:

CHORUS

I won't { have to cross Jor-dan a - lone, { Je-sus
{ have to cross Jor-dan a - lone,

died for my sins to a - tone; *(Hum)* Mm

SOLO When the darkness I see, He'll be

waiting for me

Mm   I won't have to cross Jor - dan a - lone

Em   C#7   D   Em   B7   Em   D   A7   D

2. Oftentimes I'm forsaken, and weary and sad,
   When it seems that my friends have all gone,
   There is one thought that cheers me and makes my heart glad
   I won't have to cross Jordan alone:

3. Though the billows of sorrow and trouble may sweep,
   Christ the Saviour will care for His own;
   Till the end of the journey, my soul He will keep,
   I won't have to cross Jordan alone:

   Chorus

136. This world is not my home

Traditional *arr.* G.R. Timms

1. This world is not my home, I'm just a - pass - ing through; My

G   G7   C   G

treasures are laid up Some - where be - yond the blue; The Sav - iour beckons me From

A7   D   D7   G   Em   G

hea - ven's op - en door, And I can't feel at home In this world an - y more.

C   G   C   G   A9   D   G

CHORUS

O Lord, you know, I have no friend like you; If hea-ven's not my home Then, Lord what will I do? The Saviour beckons me From hea-ven's op-en door, And I can't feel at home in this world an-y more.

2. They're all expecting me,
   And that's one thing I know,
   My Saviour pardoned me,
   Now onward I must go;
   I know He'll take me through
   Though I am weak and poor,
   And I can't feel at home
   In this world any more.
   Chorus

3. Just over in glory land
   We'll live eternally,
   The saints on every hand
   Are shouting victory;
   Their songs of sweetest praise
   Drift back from heaven's shore,
   And I can't feel at home
   In this world any more.
   Chorus

Spirituals

137. O sinner man

Traditional
arr. (piano) D.G. Wilson

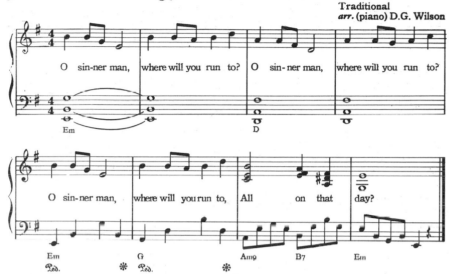

O sin-ner man, where will you run to? O sin-ner man, where will you run to?

O sin-ner man, where will you run to, All on that day?

Start with chorus

1. Run to the rocks, rocks won't you hide me?
   Run to the rocks, rocks won't you hide me?
   Run to the rocks, rocks won't you hide me,
   All on that day?

   Chorus

2. Run to the sea, sea is a-boiling,
   Run to the sea, sea is a-boiling,
   Run to the sea, sea is a-boiling,
   All on that day?

   Chorus

3. Run to the Lord, Lord won't you hide me?
   Run to the Lord, Lord won't you hide me?
   Run to the Lord, Lord won't you hide me,
   All on that day?

   Chorus

4. O sinner man, should bin a-praying,
   O sinner man, should bin a-praying,
   O sinner man, should bin a-praying,
   All on that day?

   Chorus

137. O sinner man

Traditional
arr. (vocal) M.C.T. Strover

CHORUS

O sin-ner man, where will you run to? O sin-ner man, where will you run to?

(Hum) Mm   Mm   Mm   Mm

End with chorus

M

138. If religion were a thing

Traditional (African)
arr. C. Simmonds

2. Christ died for us all, He died upon the tree,
   But now He lives, He lives in me:
   Chorus

3. We praise Thee, O God, we acknowledge Thee
   To be the Lord, the Lord most high:
   Chorus

Alternative version

1. Our Father which art in heaven
   Hallowed be Thy Name; Thy kingdom come,
   Chorus

2. Thy will be done in earth as in heaven
   Put us not to the test, lead us not into wrong.
   Chorus

139. You've got to walk that lonesome valley

Traditional *arr.* G. R. Timms

2. You've got to face one day your Maker,
   You've got to face Him by yourself;
   And no one here can face Him for you,
   You've got to face Him by yourself.

3. You've got to stand one day in Judgement,
   You've got to stand there by yourself;
   And no one here can stand there for you,
   You've got to stand there by yourself.

4. You've got to walk that lonesome valley,
   You've got to walk there by yourself;
   And no one here can walk there for you,
   You've got to walk there by yourself.

140. Were you there when
they crucified my Lord?

Traditional *arr*. P.C. Butler

Were you there when they cru-ci-fied my Lord?_____ Were you

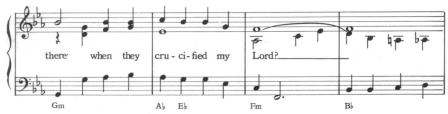

there when they cru-ci-fied my Lord?_____

Oh!_____ Sometimes it causes me to tremble, tremble

trem-ble. Were you there when they cru-ci-fied my Lord?

2. Were you there when they nailed Him to the tree?..

3. Were you there when they pierced Him in the side?..

4. Were you there when the sun refused to shine?..

5. Were you there when they laid Him in the tomb?..

6. Were you there when He rose up from the dead?
Were you there when He rose up from the dead?
O-o-oh! Sometimes I feel like shouting glory,
glory, glory.
Were you there when He rose up from the dead?

141. Steal away

Traditional *arr.* M.C.T. Strover

2. Green trees are bending,
   The sinner stands a-trembling;
   The trumpet sounds within my soul;
   I ain't got long to stay here:

   Chorus

3. My Lord He calls me;
   He calls me by the lightning
   The trumpet sounds within my soul;
   I ain't got long to stay here:'

   Chorus

142. Do you love my Lord?

Traditional *arr.* G. R. Timms

2. Makes us feel like shouting when you love my Jesus;
    Makes us feel like shouting when you love my Lord:
    I want to know, yes, I want to know,
    Do you love my Lord?
    Chorus

3. Shout it from the mountains if you love my Jesus;
    Sing it in the valleys if you love my Lord:
    I want to know, yes, I want to know,
    Do you love my Lord?
    Chorus

143. Little David

Traditional *arr.* M.C.T. Strover

N.B. Some sing as the chorus: Little David followed the Lord,
Why don't you? Why don't you?

Start with chorus

Chorus Little David, play on your harp,
Hallelu, Hallelu,
Little David play on your harp,
Hallelu.

1. Little David was a shepherd boy;
He killed Goliath, shouted for joy:
Chorus

2. Joshua was the son of Nun,
He never would quit till the work was done:
Chorus

144. The gospel train

Traditional *arr.* M.C.T. Strover

When possible, this should be performed with two guitars, one taking the bass
figure, the other the harmony of the voice part, and 'engine whistle' chords.

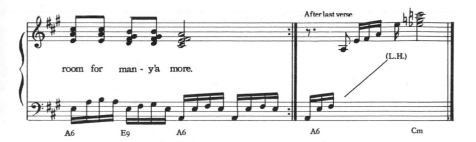

room for   man - y'a   more.

A6   E9   A6   A6   Cm

2. I hear the bell and whistle, a-coming round the curve,
   She's playing all the steam and power, and straining every nerve:
   Chorus

3. The fare is cheap and all can go, the rich and poor are there,
   No second class aboard that train, no difference in the fare:
   Chorus

4. No signal for another train to follow on the line,
   O sinner, you're for ever lost if once you're left behind:
   Chorus

5. She's nearing now the station— O sinner, don't be vain;
   O come and get your ticket, and be ready for that train:
   Chorus

145. Lord I want to be a Christian in my heart

Traditional *arr.* G. R. Timms

Lord, I want to be a Christian in my

D   G6   A9   D   G   D   D   G6   A7

1. Lord, I want to be a Christian in my heart, in my heart,
    Lord, I want to be a Christian in my heart,
    In my heart, in my heart,
    Lord, I want to be a Christian in my heart.

2. Lord, I want to be more loving in my heart...

3. Lord, I want to be more holy in my heart...

4. Lord, I want to be like Jesus in my heart...

146. Joshua fought the battle of Jericho

Traditional *arr.* M.C.T. Strover

147. Goin' to lay down my burden

Traditional *arr.* G. R. Timms

2. Goin' to lay down my sword and shield ...

3. Goin' to try on my long white robe ...

4. Goin' to try on my starry crown ...

Alternative version

1. Goin' to lay down my burden ...

2. Goin' to sing for my Saviour ...

3. Goin' to talk to my Maker ...

4. Goin' to follow my Master ...

148. Somebody's knocking at your door

Traditional *arr.* M.C.T. Strover

3. Can't you hear Him?
Somebody's knocking at your door;
Can't you hear Him?
Somebody's knocking at your door.
O sinner, why don't you answer?
Somebody's knocking at your door.

4. Answer Jesus,
Somebody's knocking at your door;
Answer Jesus,
Somebody's knocking at your door.
O sinner, why don't you answer?
Somebody's knocking at your door.

149. There is a balm in Gilead

Traditional *arr.* P.C. Butler

Start with chorus

Chorus There is a balm in Gilead
To make the wounded whole,
There is a balm in Gilead
To heal the sin-sick soul.

1. Sometimes I feel discouraged
And think my work's in vain,
But then the Holy Spirit
Revives my soul again:
Chorus

2. You cannot sing like angels,
You cannot preach like Paul,
But you can tell of Jesus
And say He died for all:
Chorus

© Copyright in this arrangement by P.C. Butler 1964 By kind permission

150. Go tell it on the mountain

Traditional *arr.* P.C.Butler

2. He made me a watchman,
   Upon the city wall;
   To tell of His salvation,
   For Jesus died for all:
   Chorus

3. Go tell it to your neighbour
   In darkness here below;
   Go with the words of Jesus,
   That all the world may know:
   Chorus

INDEX OF TITLES AND FIRST LINES

The first line of a piece is included, in italic type, only where it differs from the title.